POWER BLOCK IDEAS FOR TEACHERS

Center for Innovation in Education

Principal Writer & Editor
Richard Cossen

Illustrator
Steven Dore

TABLE OF CONTENTS

ACKNOWLEDGMENTS

Power Blocks were developed by the Center for Innovation in Education. The Center invited teachers from kindergarten through high school to participate in the development of curriculum to accompany the blocks. The activities that follow are examples of the kinds of things these teachers did with their blocks. I would like to acknowledge the contributions of the following teachers whose ideas are used in whole or in part in the development of this book:

Vicki Axford	Barbara Hackney	Ruth Patrick
Janet Baird	Mary Ann Hagen	Karen Pinkham
Juanita Bass	Darci Hammond	Judy Ray
Dorothy Beck	Karen Jenkins	Mary Roberts
Betsy Berry	Doreen Junk	Patrice Rogers
Jean Black	Judy Keller	Claire Rotolo
Bess Bloyer	Jan Korr	Charlotte Schell
Judy Blum	Betty Kovacs	Paula Scull
Carol Brittin-Sasek	Nancy Kraft	Stasia Simrall
Nancy Brooks	Nancy Leafdale	Elaine Sparks
Patti Buehman	Sandra Leatherwood	Sandy Starr
Cindy Catignani	Shirley Leendertsen	Mary Ann Stine
Candy Chaplin	Kim McColman	Kris Strandness
Karen Chong	Mary Ann Mead	Lynn Sullivan
Nancy Coville	Judy Meyer	Jane Tod
Margo Dahlstrom	Jane Miller	Jane Traut
Syrel Dawson	Mary Nauyokas	Kara Trumbo
Thor Fridriksson	Beverly Newsome	Sandra Unrau
Mary Griffith	Chris Noble	Mary Van Valin Clark
Wilsene Grout	Kevin O'Connor	Andrea Varon
Kathie Grzesiak	Marguerite Packnett	Bobbie Vruggink

I would also like to thank the following people who read and edited the early drafts: **Bob Baratta-Lorton, Kathie Bunn, Alôna Harvey, Susan Iwamoto, Naomi Izumizaki,** and **Tammy Pourroy**. Each provided valuable help in tidying up this project. In many cases, their efforts resulted in a total "vacuuming" of the text. If errors or ambiguities occur in this version, it is only because I have gone back to the edited text and made additional changes without consulting them.

INTRODUCTION

A set of Power Blocks consists of 254 blocks cut in the shape of triangles, squares, rectangles, and parallelograms. They are produced in eight different colors. Sets of different colors may be mixed or left intact. Eight sets are a useful quantity for a class of thirty-two students. One reason for leaving the sets intact is to facilitate whole class instruction. Frequently within a class, each group of students needs the larger blocks to solve a problem. There are fewer of the larger shapes than the smaller shapes. Having each set a different color enables the teacher and students to locate missing blocks quickly.

Power Blocks are cut to metric units. The basic unit of length is the length of the side of the smallest square, which is 25 millimeters. Each of the different pieces is inscribed with a code to identify it. Ten different triangles are coded T1 through T10. Squares are coded S1 through S5. Rectangles are coded R1 through R5. Parallelograms are coded P1 through P4. The breakdown of the pieces in a set is as follows:

Triangles	Qty		Squares	Qty
T1	32		S1	100
T2	16		S2	4
T3	8		S3	2
T4	8		S4	4
T5	4		S5	4
T6	8		**Total Squares**	**114**
T7	4			
T8	2		**Rectangles**	**Qty**
T9	2		R1	8
T10	2		R2	4
Total Triangles	**86**		R3	2
			R4	2
Parallelograms	**Qty**		R5	2
P1	16		**Total Rectangles**	**18**
P2	8			
P3	8			
P4	4			
Total Parallelograms	**36**			

Each set of Power Blocks has within it all the pieces required to make four separate Tangram Puzzles. Each set also includes one hundred square tiles.

The shapes have been designed around the pattern for the powers of two (1, 2, 4, 8, 16, 32...). The powers of two pattern also occurs when exploring base two numbers. Elements of the powers of two pattern also occur frequently in the writing and development of computer programs and the design of microprocessors. Power Blocks and the traditional Pattern Blocks are not redundant. Pattern Blocks are cut to the square number pattern (1, 4, 9, 16, 25, 36,..). The two materials are meant to complement and not replace one another.

In the lessons that follow, I have assumed teachers are working with small groups of students or are working from an overhead projector. Overhead Power Blocks are not presently commercially available. However, it is possible to make a set. If you are interested in doing this, purchase the following items from an artist's supply store:

> Utility knife (extra blades)
> Cutting mat
> Fine tipped permanent marking pen

Use the yellow pages in your local phone book to locate a plastics store that sells clear vinyl. Vinyl is soft and flexible and can be cut without using a power saw. Purchase enough one-eighth inch thick clear vinyl to make the blocks you want to make.

> Place the vinyl on the cutting mat
> Place a Power Block on the vinyl
> Cut around the Power Block
> Write the block's code on the vinyl

Repeat the process for each block you need.

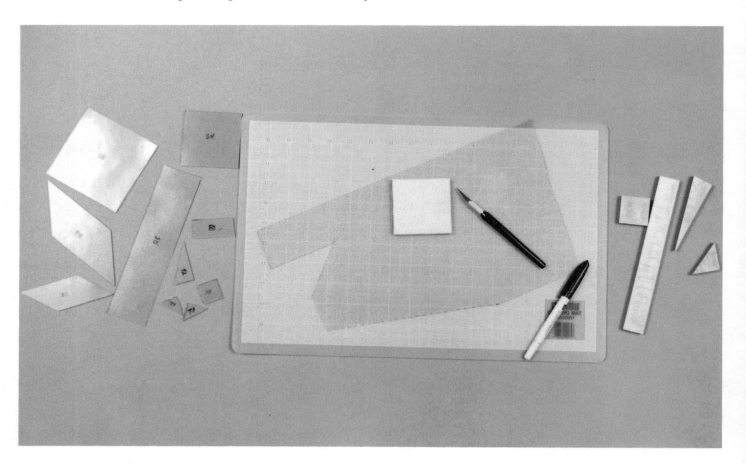

ATTRIBUTES

The activities in this chapter flow naturally from students' unstructured explorations. Students will intuitively sort and classify the blocks without direction from the teacher. The lessons that follow will direct students' attention to identifying and describing specific Power Block attributes.

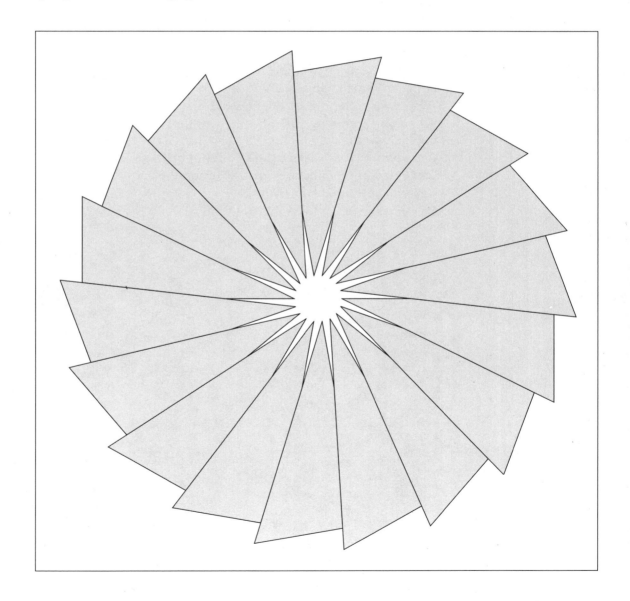

SORTING AND CLASSIFYING

Materials:_____Power Blocks (mixed colors)
Yarn loops

Purpose: _____To sort a set of blocks in different ways

Activity: _____**Teacher**: Can you think of a way to sort your blocks?
Student: Sure.
Teacher: How would you sort them?
Student: Sort them by color?
Teacher: Okay. Try it. Can someone suggest a different way to sort the blocks?
Student: By shape.
Teacher: How many different shapes are there in your set?
Student: I don't know.
Teacher: Use the loops of yarn to surround groups of blocks with the same attribute.

Questions to explore with students:

– When you sorted by shape, how did you decide what it meant to be a different shape? Is T1 the same shape as T3? If so, why?

– When you sorted by shape, how many different shapes did you find?

– When you sorted by size, how many different size triangles, squares, rectangles, and parallelograms did you find?

– Can you sort the blocks by their interior angles?

– Can you sort the blocks by their exterior angles?

– Can you sort them by perimeter?

– Can you sort them by area?

GUESS MY BLOCK

Materials: _____ Power Blocks (T2, T4, S2, S4, P2, P4, R2, and R4)

Purpose: _____ To identify a specific hidden block from a list of clues

Activity: _____ Before the lesson, divide the Power Blocks into groups so there is a large and small example of each shape. Place each group in a sock, bag, or box. Each container should have the same set of blocks.

Teacher: I am going to reach into my bag and find one block. I will describe it to you without looking at it. Reach into your bag and see if you can find the block I am talking about. Don't take it out until I have finished giving the clues.
> It is small.
> It has four sides.
> It has four right angles.
> It has two sides longer than the other two sides.

Now take out the block you think I have described.
Students: Okay.
Teacher: Did all of us take out the same block?
Students: No.
Teacher: Why not?

When students can identify blocks described by the teacher, they may describe a block and have their classmates identify it.

Questions to explore with students:
– What would happen if we added more blocks to our set?
– Which blocks shall we add?

DESCRIPTIONS

Materials: _____ Power Blocks

Purpose: _____ To generate a list of attributes that uniquely describes a given block

Activity: _____ This activity is essentially the same as the activity outlined on pages 200-202 of *Mathematics...A Way of Thinking*.[1] In the activity described in *Mathematics...A Way of Thinking*, students write descriptions that uniquely describe themselves. The teacher collects all the descriptions and selects one to read to the class. The class stands, and the teacher reads the description one attribute at a time. As each attribute is read, students for whom it is not true take their seats. The goal is to have the student who wrote the description be the only one left standing after the last attribute is read.

Teacher: Choose a block. Write statements that describe your block. Number each statement. You cannot use its code to describe a block. When you have finished writing, I will collect all the papers.
Students: How many statements do we need to write?

[1]Baratta-Lorton, Robert. Mathematics ... A Way Of Thinking. Reading, MA: Addison-Wesley Publishing Company.

Teacher: As many as you need to describe your block.
Students: Okay.
Teacher: Pass your papers to me.
Students: Okay.
Teacher: Everyone please stand up. Now I will read one of the descriptions. If the statement I read is true for your block, stay standing. If it is not, sit down. It has four sides. Who should sit down?
Student: Anyone who described a triangle.
Teacher: It has four right angles. Who should sit down?
Student: Those who described parallelograms.
Teacher: It is not a square. Who should sit down?
Students: Anyone with a square.
Teacher: It is red. Who should sit down?
Student: People who have other colors.
Teacher: It is one-half S5. Who is left standing?
Student: Those with red R4.
Teacher: How many people?
Student: Two.
Teacher: Only those with R4s are left. The R4s were uniquely described in terms of the group of blocks we chose to describe.

Questions to explore with students:

- What is the fewest number of statements that you can write and still uniquely describe a block?
- Is there more than one way to uniquely describe a block? If so, how many can you find?
- Do all blocks have the same number of ways?

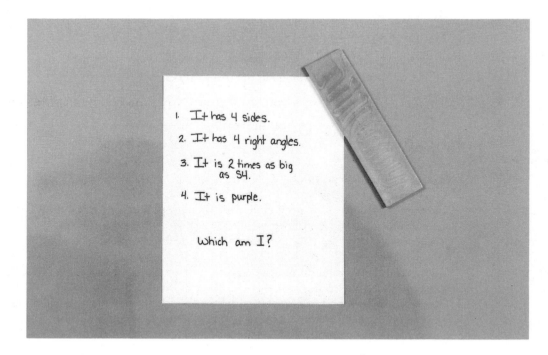

FIND A RULE

Materials: _____ Power Blocks (at least two sets of different colors)
Yarn loops

Purpose: _____ To sort blocks by two attributes into two mutually exclusive groups

Activity: _____ **Teacher**: S4 goes in the green loop. P4 also goes in the green loop. T3 goes in the orange loop. Where do you think S1 will go?
Student: In the green loop with S4.
Teacher: Yes, by my rule it will go in the green loop. What about R2? Where will it go?
Student: In the green loop with S4 and P4.
Teacher: Where do you think I will put T7?
Student: In the orange loop with T3.
Teacher: That fits my rule. Do you know a rule that would work?
Student: Blocks with four sides go in the green loop. If it is a triangle it goes in the orange loop with T3.
Teacher: Yes, that fits what we have done. Is there another rule that would fit?
Student: Shapes with four right angles go in the green loop, and shapes with one right angle go in the orange loop.
Teacher: That works too. Can anyone think of a different rule that would work?

When students can sort objects that have a single attribute in common from the balance of the blocks, they may attempt more complex sorts.

Teacher: See if you can determine a rule that works. Yellow S4 goes in the green loop. Blue R1 goes in the orange loop. Yellow P4 goes in the green loop. Blue R5 goes in the orange loop. Where do you think blue T1 will go?
Student: In the orange loop.
Teacher: What rule did you use to place it there?
Student: Yellows in the green loop, blues in the orange loop.
Teacher: That's a good rule, but by my rule I would put blue T1 in the green loop. Where would yellow T3 go?
Student: In the green loop.
Teacher: Why?
Student: Because it is yellow and only blues are in the orange loop.
Teacher: O.K. Where would blue P4 go?
Student: I don't know.
Teacher: By my rule it would go in the green loop. Where would blue R5 go?
Student: I don't know.
Teacher: By my rule it would go in the orange loop.
Student: I know a rule that works. All blue rectangles go in the orange loop and the rest of the blocks go in the green loop.
Teacher: That seems to work. Where would blue R4 go?
Student: In the orange loop.
Teacher: Yes, that's where I would put it by my rule. Is there another rule that would fit this situation?

Questions to explore with students:

– How many different ways can you sort the blocks when one group has one attribute in common?

– How many ways can you sort the blocks when one group has two attributes in common?

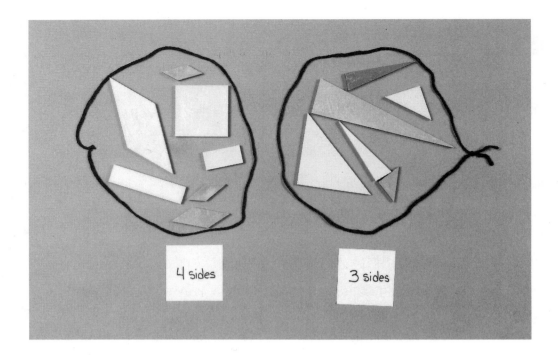

VENN DIAGRAMS

Materials: _____ Power Blocks (two sets of different colors)
Small cards or pieces of paper (3 x 5)
Yarn loops

Purpose: _____ To sort and classify blocks using a Venn diagram

Activity: _____ This activity is essentially the same as that outlined in *Mathematics Their Way*[2] on pages 84 through 87. Students create a set of cards, each of which lists an attribute of a set of objects contained in a sorting box. They take two cards at random from the stack and sort as many of the objects as they can into two groups. They must deal with the problem that occurs when an object has both attributes listed on the cards. Before the lesson, the teacher sorts the blocks into smaller groups composed of two or three large triangles in each color, two or three medium size triangles in each color, and two or three small triangles in each color. Do the same thing for each of the other square, rectangle, and parallelogram shapes .

Teacher: Think of ways to sort the blocks in your set. I will write the ways on the overhead. Does anyone have an idea of one way to sort the blocks?
Student: By color.
Teacher: Okay. Does anyone have a different idea?
Student: We can sort by size.
Teacher: Okay. Can anyone think of another way?
Student: By number of sides.
Student: By shape.
Student: By those that have right angles and those that do not.
Student: By...

---

[2]Baratta-Lorton, Mary. <u>Mathematics Their Way</u>. Reading, MA: Addison-Wesley Publishing Company.

Teacher: Now that our list is complete, write each suggestion on a different card.

Student: Finished.

Teacher: Shuffle your cards, and then pick two. Put all the blocks with the same attribute listed on the card inside a loop of yarn. Then pick another card and put all the blocks that have that attribute in the second loop.

Student: Some of the blocks could go in both loops. Which loop should I put them in?

Teacher: Is there a way to arrange them so that they are in both loops?

When students have sorted by two attributes, have them sort by three. They may leave the cards with the attributes listed on them face down close to the loops of yarn. Other students may look at the sorts and try to predict the attributes used to sort the blocks. Students turn over the cards to check their predictions.

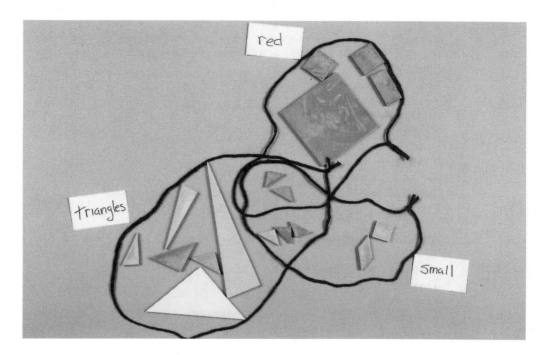

QUESTIONS

Materials: _____ Power Blocks

Purpose: _____ To identify a specific block from student generated questions

Activity: _____ **Teacher:** We are going to play a game that requires asking good questions. One half of the class is on one team, and the other half of the class is the other team. I have chosen one Power Block for you to identify. The first team to identify the mystery block is the winner. You can only ask me questions that can be answered with a yes or no. If I answer your question with a yes, the next person on your team gets to ask a question. If I answer the question with a no, the other team gets to ask a question. You cannot give helpful hints to your teammates. If you ask me if it is a specific block and it is not the correct block, the other team gets a point. If you guess the block, your team gets a point.

Student on first team: Is it green?
Teacher: No.
Student on second team: Is it a square?
Teacher: No.
Student on first team: Is it red?
Teacher: Yes.
Student on first team: Is it P4?
Teacher: No. That's one point for the other team.
Student on second team: Is it a triangle?
Teacher: Yes.
Student on second team: Is it smaller than T4?
Teacher: Yes.
Student on second team: Is it smaller than T3?
Teacher: No.
Student on first team: Is it T3?
Teacher: No. That's one for the other team.
Student on second team: Is it T7?
Teacher: Yes. One more point for your team.

Questions to explore with students:

– What strategy did you use to help you decide what question to ask?
– Is one strategy of asking questions more helpful than other strategies?

ATTRIBUTE TRAINS

Materials: _____ Power Blocks (at least two sets of different colors)
Lined paper

Purpose: _____ To build a train of blocks where each succeeding block is one attribute different from the previous block

Activity: _____ For this activity, it is useful for students to have completed the activities that enable them to create a table of relative areas because they need to know which shapes have the same areas.

Teacher: I want you to work in teams of two. Fold your paper so that it has three columns. Write the word "color" at the top of one column, and the words "shape" and "size" at the top of each of the other columns. Pick one block to start your train.
Student: Any block?
Teacher: Yes. Record its color, size, and shape in the columns on your paper.
Student : Okay.
Teacher: Now choose another block that is the same color and shape, but a different size. Record the information about this block.
Student: Done.
Teacher: This time, pick a block that is the same size and same shape, but a different color than the block I just put down.
Student: Okay.
Teacher: Record its color, size, and shape. Take turns adding pieces to your train. I want you to make your train of blocks as long as you can. Be sure that each new piece follows the pattern "same, same, different". That is, two attributes are the same and one attribute is different from the previous block.

When students understand how to make trains with one different attribute between each step, ask them to make trains that have two differences between each step.

Questions to explore with students:

– If you stack blocks on top of one another, for example two T4s, so you had blocks of different thicknesses, could you make trains that followed the pattern "same, same, same, different"?

– If you can make trains of blocks with four attributes, can you make one with the pattern "different, different, different, same"?

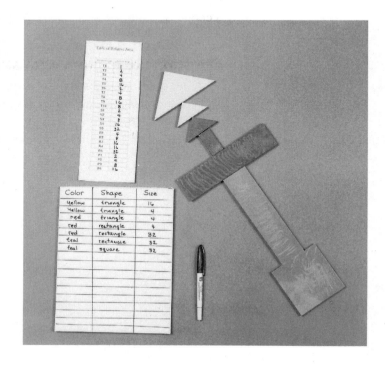

ATTRIBUTES ON A MATRIX

*Materials:*_____ Power Blocks (at least three sets of different colors)
Large piece of paper (12 x 18 inches)

Purpose: _____ To place blocks in a three by three array so that each block has two attributes different from those immediately next to it

Activity: _____ For this activity, it is useful for students to have completed the activities that enable them to create a table of relative area because they need to know which shapes have the same area.

Teacher: Fold your paper so that you have a matrix with three columns and three rows.
Student: Okay.
Teacher: Choose one block and place it in the upper left hand corner of your matrix.
Student: Any block?
Teacher: Yes. Now I want you to find another block that has two attributes that are different from the attributes of the first block. Put that block in the space immediately to the right of the first block. For example, your block might be a "different color" and "different shape".
Student : Okay.
Teacher: Now find a block that has two attributes that are different from the first block and place it in the space below the first block.
Student: This takes thinking.
Teacher: Now for the final step, see if you can find a block to put in the space that is below and to the right of the last two blocks you put down. This block must be two attributes different from the block above it and two attributes different from the block to the left of it.
Student: Can we go back and change one of the other blocks if we can't find a block to work?
Teacher: Yes. The idea is to fill in the matrix. Sometimes you have to move things around to make it work. When you have finished one matrix, get another piece of paper and try it again with a different block.

Students may take small pieces of paper or sticky labels to record the attributes that are the same or different between two blocks. They place these between the two blocks on the matrix. When students can do a three by three matrix, they may try a four by four matrix.

Questions to explore with students:

– Can you make an array in which each block is one different?
– What would happen if you stack blocks so that you added the attribute of thickness to the attributes you are working with?
– What would happen if you were to add another set of blocks of a different color? Would the task be more difficult?
– What would happen if you tried to make an array in which each block was three different?

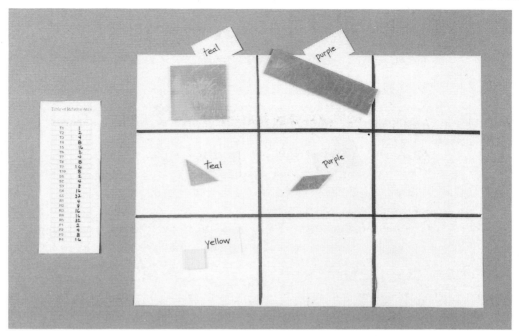

BUILDING BEHIND A SHIELD

Materials: _____ Power Blocks
Shields (file folders work nicely)

Purpose: _____ To build a shape from verbal directions given by another person

Activity: _____ The level of difficulty of this activity may be controlled by limiting the number of block students use in their designs?

Teacher: I am going to make a shape behind this shield so that you cannot see what I am building. I want you to build what I describe. Build your shape behind your shield so that other students cannot see what you are building. When I have finished giving directions, everyone will lift their shields at the same time and we will see what has been built. You cannot ask questions. If you do, I will not answer them.

Place the S4 so one edge is parallel to the edge of your desk.
Student: Okay.
Teacher: Next, find a triangle that has two sides that are equal to the length of the side of the square. Put the top of the triangle against the top edge of the square. The right angle of the triangle must be against the top left hand corner of the square.
Student: Can I stand the triangle up?
Teacher: Remember no questions may be asked. Find a parallelogram that has its longest side equal to the length of the side of the square.
Student: Found it.
Teacher: Place the parallelogram against the left side of the square. Match the side of the parallelogram and square that are touching so they are the same length. The pointed end of the parallelogram must extend below the bottom to the square.
Student: Okay.

Teacher: Continue giving directions until the shape is completely described. Then tell everyone to "Lift your shields". Did everyone make the same shape?
Student: No.
Teacher: What could I have done to make my directions clearer?

When students understand how to build a shape described by the teacher, they may work in groups. One student takes a turn playing the teacher's role, the others build. When the directions are finished, all the students lift their shields to see the results.

Questions to explore with students:

- What would happen if we played the game and let students ask the teacher questions that can be answered with a yes or no?
- Was the game easier?
- What are the important things for those who are giving the directions to do?
- What are the important things for those who are following the directions to do?

GEOMETRY

The activities in this chapter encourage students to acquire the vocabulary to describe shapes in terms of their geometric properties. The activities also encourage students to explore the concepts of symmetry, congruency and similarity.

POLYGONS: IDENTIFYING SIDES

Materials: _____ Power Blocks
Unlined paper
Centimeter cubes or beans

Purpose: _____ To identify the sides of a shape

Activity: _____ **Teacher**: Today we are going to study the sides of a shape. I want to mark each side of R5 with a centimeter cube. How many sides do you think R5 has?
Student: Four.
Teacher: I will mark each side by putting a centimeter cube as close to its middle as I can. How many cubes have I put around R5?
Student: Four.
Teacher: I want you to mark the sides of as many Power Blocks as you can.

When students can identify the sides of Power Blocks, they will learn to identify the sides of more elaborate polygons.

Teacher: I have built this shape with R5 and T5. We are going to identify its sides. The sides are the outside edges of this shape. Do not look inside the shape for sides. Pretend the shape is made from one piece of plastic. How many sides do you think it has?
Student: Five.
Teacher: How did you get five?
Student: I counted them.
Teacher: How did you know what to count?
Student: I touched each side and counted.
Teacher: How did you know where the next side was?
Student: When the side turned, then it was a new side.

When students understand what is required, they work together building polygons. They mark the sides with centimeter cubes or beans. They may trace their polygons and mark sides with a symbol of some kind.

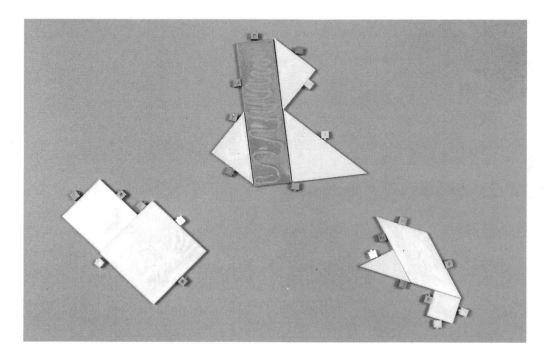

Questions to explore with students:
- Can you make a shape with five sides?
- Can you make a shape with six sides?
- What is the shape with the fewest sides?

POLYGONS: CONVEX AND CONCAVE POLYGONS

*Materials:*_____ Power Blocks
Unlined paper
Centimeter cubes or beans

Purpose: _____ To identify shapes that are convex or concave

Activity: _____ **Teacher**: Here are two shapes P4 and T5. When I put them together like this, they make a trapezoid.

Now watch what happens when I change the shape.

If I put T5 and P4 together like this, the polygon has a dent in it. If a polygon has sides like the trapezoid, then it is convex. If it has sides that push in (make a dent) then it is concave.
Student: Are those the only two ways polygons can be?
Teacher: Let's find out. I want you to make as many polygons with your blocks as you can. If it is convex, don't do anything to it. If it is concave, put a centimeter cube at the point of the dent.

When students understand what is required, they work together building polygons. They identify them as either convex or concave. They mark the concave sides with cubes or beans. They may trace and label their polygons to make a record of what they have done.

Questions to explore with students:
- Can you make a convex shape with five sides?
- Can you make a concave shape with five sides?
- Which are easier to make with the blocks, convex or concave shapes? Why?
- Can you make a concave shape with three sides?
- If you can, how did you do it? If you can't, why not?
- Make a convex shape with as many sides as you can. How many sides does it have?
- Make a concave shape with as many sides as you can. How many sides does it have?

POLYGONS: IDENTIFYING INTERIOR ANGLES

Materials:_____ Power Blocks
Unlined paper
Centimeter cubes or beans

Purpose: _____ To identify the interior angles of a shape

Activity: _____ **Teacher**: Today we are going to learn about interior angles. When two straight lines meet, angles are formed. Watch what happens when I trace T5 like this. Notice how the sides meet at a point. The space between the two sides and the point they meet is called an angle. Take out R5. Put a centimeter cube on top of each of the shape's interior angles. How many angles did you find?
Student: Four.
Teacher: Good. I want you to mark the interior angles of as many Power Blocks as you can.

When students can identify the interior angles of Power Blocks, they will learn to identify the interior angles of more elaborate polygons.

Teacher: I have built this shape with S5 and T5.

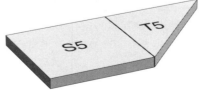

How many interior angles do you think it has?

Student: Four.
Teacher: Show me.
Students: I put a cube on each corner like this:

When students understand what is required, they work together building polygons. They mark the interior angles with cubes or beans. They may trace their polygons and mark the interior angles. The complexity of the polygons they make can be controlled by limiting the number of blocks they use to build a given shape. The interior angles of concave shapes may prove a little more difficult to identify, but with practice they will identify them as quickly as they do the other angles.

Questions to explore with students:

- Can you make a shape with five interior angles?
- Can you make a shape with six interior angles?
- What is the shape with the fewest interior angles?
- What is the largest number of interior angles you have in one shape?
- Can you make a shape with one more interior angle than your previous shape?

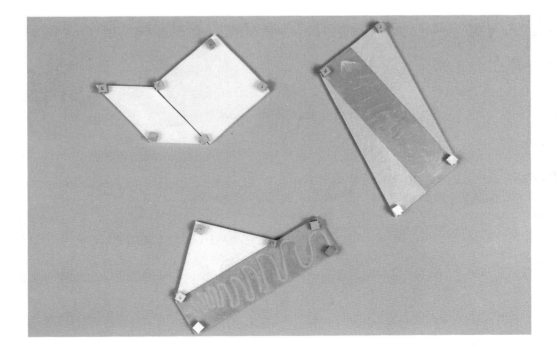

POLYGONS: IDENTIFYING EXTERIOR ANGLES

Materials: _____ Power Blocks
Unlined paper
Centimeter cubes or beans

Purpose: _____ To identify the exterior angles of a shape

Activity: _____ **Teacher:** Today we are going to study exterior angles. Watch me as I put a centimeter cube at each exterior angle of R5. How many cubes have I put beside R5?
Students: Four.
Teacher: If you had to tell friends how to find the exterior angles of a polygon, how would you tell them?
Student: I would tell them that the exterior angles are the corners.
Teacher: I want you to mark the exterior angles of as many Power Blocks as you can. Put a centimeter cube at each exterior angle.

When students can identify the exterior angles of Power Blocks, they learn to identify the exterior angles of more elaborate polygons.

Teacher: I have built this shape with R5 and T5. Estimate with centimeter cubes how many exterior angles you think it has...

Let's see. I will place a cube at each angle. How many cubes are there?
Students: Six.
Teacher: Which angle do you think is the hardest one to remember to count?
Student: The one where the sides bend in.
Teacher: How can we identify the exterior angles?
Students: They are at the corners.

When students understand what is required, they work together building polygons. They mark the exterior angles with cubes or beans. They may trace their polygons and mark the exterior angles.

Questions to explore with students:

- Can you make a shape with five exterior angles?
- Can you make a shape with six exterior angles?
- What is the shape with the fewest exterior angles?
- What is the largest number of exterior angles you have in one shape?
- Can you make a shape with one more exterior angle than your previous shape?

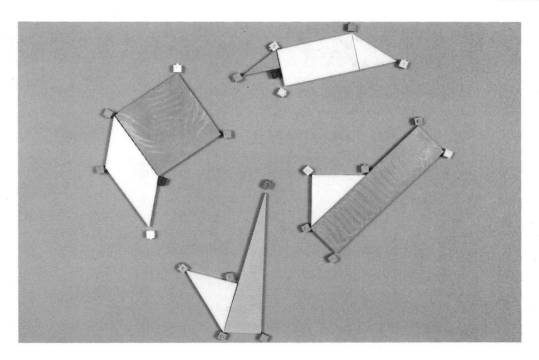

POLYGONS: PREDICTING SIDES AND ANGLES

*Materials:*_____Power Blocks
Unlined paper
Centimeter cubes or beans

Purpose: _____To identify the relationship between the number of sides, interior, and exterior angles

Activity: _____**Teacher**: Write these headings on your paper.

Sides   Interior Exterior

I have made this polygon from R4, S3, and T3.

Teacher: How many sides does it have?
Student: Six.
Teacher: Record it like this.

Sides   Interior Exterior
   6

How many interior angles does it have?
Student: Six.
Teacher: Record it like this:

Sides	Interior	Exterior
6	6	

Teacher: How many exterior angles does it have?
Student: 6
Teacher: Record it like this:

Sides	Interior	Exterior
6	6	6

Use your set of blocks to make as many polygons as you can. Record the number of sides, interior angles, and exterior angles on your paper.

When students have gathered their data the teacher consolidates it into a table.

Sides	Interior	Exterior
6	6	6
3	3	3
7	7	7
9	9...	

Teacher: Do you see a pattern? If you knew the number of sides a polygon has, could you predict the number of interior angles it has?

Questions to explore with students:

– Can you predict the number of exterior angles if you know the number of sides?
– Can you predict the number of interior angles if you know the number of exterior angles?

© 1993 Center for Innovation in Education, Saratoga, California

CONGRUENT POWER BLOCKS

Materials: _____ Power Blocks
Unlined paper

Purpose: _____ To create congruent Power Block shapes

Activity: _____ **Teacher**: Today we are going to make shapes that are congruent. Congruent shapes are copies of one another. If you look in a mirror, the reflection you see is congruent to you. (Technically, for shapes to be congruent their internal structures must also be identical. However for now, we are defining congruent as shapes having the same outline and same size.) I want you to build another shape that is the same size and shape as S5. Build it right on top of S5. Watch me. I will cover S5 with R4, S3, and two T3s.

Can anyone think of a different way to cover S5?
Students: Can anything hang over the sides?
Teacher: No. How many different ways can we make S5?

When students have explored S5, they build congruent versions of the other blocks. Students may trace their shapes to make a record of their work.

Questions to explore with students:

– How many different ways can you make a shape?
– Is there a relationship between the number of T1s it takes to make a shape and the number of ways it can be made?

RECORDING EQUATIONS FOR SHAPES

Materials: _____ Power Blocks
Unlined paper

Purpose: _____ To record congruent shapes as equations

Activity: _____ **Teacher**: We are going to study congruent shapes and make a record of what we find out. Take out P4 and trace it like this. I will build a congruent shape on top of the tracing. I will remove one block at a time and make a tracing of where it was on my tracing of P4. I will write an equation that tells how I made my shape. When I covered P4, I used three blocks. I can write that like this:

$$S3 + 2T3 = P4$$

What does this mean?
Student: An S3 and two T3s equals a P4.
Teacher: Make a tracing and write an equation for each way you can make a shape that is congruent to P4.

When students understand what is required, they work together building shapes that are congruent to specific blocks. They record their results as described above.

Questions to explore with students:

- Is it possible to have the same equation for two different ways to make a shape?
- How many different ways can you write an equation for the same block?
- Is there a relationship between the number of T1s it takes to make a shape and the number of ways it can be written as an equation?

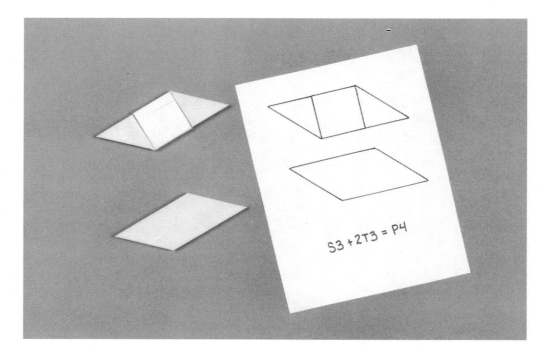

CONGRUENT SHAPES

Materials: _____ Power Blocks
Power Block triangle paper on legal size sheets

Purpose: _____ To make student generated task cards for building congruent shapes

Activity: _____ **Teacher**: Watch how I draw a polygon on the triangle paper. Notice that I must always trace on top of the lines of the triangle paper. I can go in any direction I want, as long as I don't cross over the top of the line I have just traced. I keep tracing until I get back to the point I started. Each polygon should be equal to at least sixteen little triangles. I want you to make as many polygons as you can in the next fifteen minutes.
Students: Can we draw more than one polygon on a each side of a piece of paper?
Teacher: No. I want you to limit it to only one polygon on each side of paper.

When students have finished creating polygons (about five or six per student) the teacher collects the papers. These will be used as task cards.

Teacher: Shortly, I will give you some of the drawings that you have just made. When you get them, count the number of little triangles it takes to make the polygon. Each little triangle is equal to T1. In my puzzle, there are 49 T1s . I record it like this:

$$49\,T1 =$$

I will try to cover the polygon with as few blocks as possible and then record what I have done like this:

$$49T1 = 3T1 + 2T3 + P1 + R1 + R4 + P4$$

When you get a task card, I want you to make the polygon outlined on your paper using as few blocks as possible. After you have covered your polygon, record the results. Pass the paper to a neighbor. Your neighbor is to try to make the shape using the blocks indicated in your equation. After he/she has done it your way, see if he/she can find a different way to cover the polygon.

After three or four students have tried each polygon, collect the task cards. Save them for the next activity.

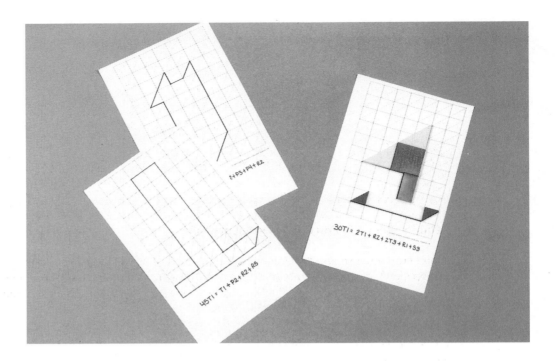

SIMPLIFYING EQUATIONS

Materials: _____ Power Blocks
Task cards from previous lessons
Table of relative areas
Lined paper
Calculators

Purpose: _____ To simplify student generated equations

Activity: _____ **Teacher**: Yesterday you wrote equations to describe polygons. The equation for the polygon I made was written as:

$$49T1 = 3T1 + 2T3 + P1 + R1 + R4 + P4$$

If T1 equals one, how much is the left side of the equation?
Student: Forty-nine.
Teacher: Why?
Student: Because forty nine ones is forty nine.
Teacher: O.K. I will record it like this:

$$49 = 3T1 + 2T3 + P1 + R1 + R4 + P4$$

How much are three T1s?
Student: Three.
Teacher: Record it like this:

$$49 = 3 + 2T3 + P1 + R1 + R4 + P4$$

How much are two T3s?

Student: Eight.

Teacher: O.K. Record it like this:

$$49 = 3 + 8 + P1 + R1 + R4 + P4$$

The process continues until the equation looks like this:

$$49 = 3 + 8 + 2 + 4 + 16 + 16$$

Use your calculators to check to see if this is true?

Student: It's true. Forty-nine equals forty-nine.

When students are comfortable with the process of simplifying equations, pass out the previous lesson's task cards. Students copy the equations from the task card on to lined paper. They record the process of simplification. If they have equations that do not balance, they may record the results like this:

$$38T1 = 3T1 + R1 + T3 + S3 + S1 + T5$$
$$38 = 3 + 4 + 4 + 8 + 2 + 16$$
$$38 \neq 37$$

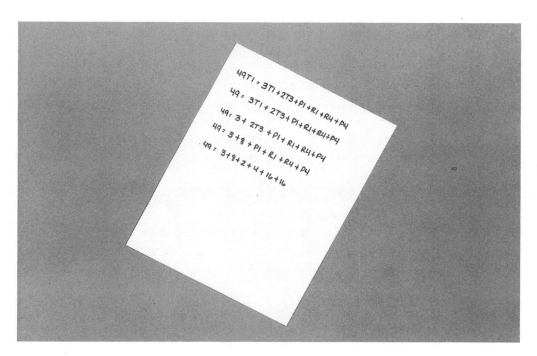

REFLECTION SYMMETRY

Materials: _____ Power Blocks
Unlined paper
Mirrors
Rulers

Purpose: _____ To identify lines of reflection symmetry in Power Blocks

Activity: _____ **Teacher**: Take out S5. Can you place your mirror on the block so the image in the mirror is exactly the same as the part of the block behind the mirror?
Student: Yes.
Teacher: How many different ways were you able to put your mirror on S5 so the reflection was identical to the part of the block that was hidden?
Student: There are two ways to put the mirror from corner to corner and two ways to put the mirror from side to side.
Teacher: Can anyone find a different way?
Trace S5 and use your ruler to draw where you put the mirror. That is the line of reflective symmetry. A shape has reflection symmetry when its mirror image is an exact copy of the part hidden by the mirror. S5 has four lines of reflection symmetry. Take out P4. Does it have lines of reflection symmetry?
Student: I can't find any.
Teacher: Why not?
Student: No matter how I place the mirror, what I see in it is different from the part behind it.

Questions to explore with students:

– Which Power Blocks have reflection symmetry?
– Which shapes do not?
– The square has four lines of reflection symmetry. Does the rectangle?
– Do you see any objects in the classroom that have reflection symmetry?
– Can you think of any objects at home that have reflection symmetry?

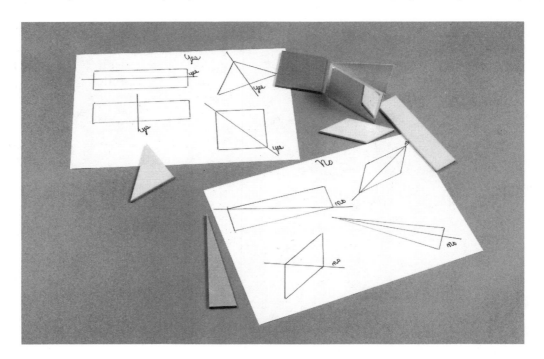

REFLECTION SYMMETRY

Materials: _____ Power Blocks
Mirrors
Rulers
Yarn

Purpose: _____ To build shapes that have reflection symmetry

Activity: _____ **Teacher**: I need someone to volunteer to work with me. I will choose a Power Block, and set it in front of us on one side of the yarn. My partner will take the same kind of block and place it beside mine on the other side of the yarn.
Student: Is there any special way that you want me to put it against your block?
Teacher: Yes. Pretend there is a mirror on the line between our two blocks. If you were to look into the mirror, you would see a reflection of my block. Place your block so that it is a reflection of my block.
Student: I get the idea.
Teacher: Let's continue to build our shape, always being careful to make sure that they are symmetrical. How could we check to be sure they are symmetrical?
Student: Use a mirror.
Teacher: Work with a partner to make shapes or designs that have reflection symmetry. Use a mirror to make sure your shapes are symmetrical.

When students understand the task of building symmetrical shapes and designs, they may make a record of what they have done by tracing their polygons and drawing in the line(s) of reflective symmetry.

Questions to explore with students:

– Remember how the square had four lines of symmetry. Can you make another shape that has four different lines of reflective symmetry?

– What shape can you make that has the most lines of reflection symmetry?

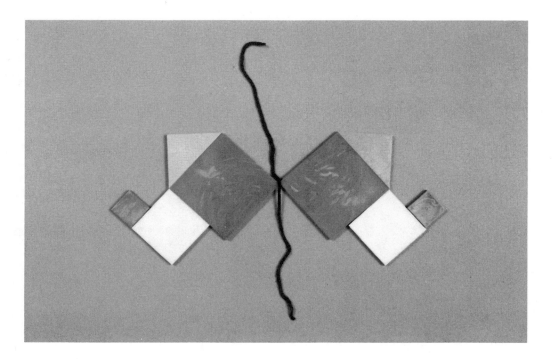

3D REFLECTION SYMMETRY

Materials:_____ Power Blocks
Yarn

Purpose: _____ To build three-dimensional shapes that have reflection symmetry

Activity: _____ **Teacher**: Up until now we have been studying two-dimensional shapes. Two-dimensional shapes are flat. They have length and width. I want you to build three-dimensional shapes. These are shapes that have length, width, and height. I am going to build a shape in three dimensions. The shape is going to have at least one line of reflection symmetry. Does anyone see a line of reflective symmetry?
Student: Yes.
Teacher: Use this piece of yarn to show where we would put a mirror.
Student: Don't we need mirrors?
Teacher: No, in this situation we will use an imaginary mirror. You can show where the mirror would cut through your shape by laying a piece of yarn across it. Build as many three-dimensional shapes with reflection symmetry as you can.

Questions to explore with students:
- Can you make a three-dimensional shape that has two different lines of reflective symmetry?
- Can you make a three-dimensional shape with more than two lines of reflective symmetry?
- Do you see any three-dimensional objects in the classroom that have reflection symmetry?
- Can you think of any objects at home that have reflection symmetry?

BUILDING SHAPES FROM REFLECTIONS

Materials: _____ Power Blocks
Unlined paper
Mirrors

Purpose: _____ To explore reflections and lines of symmetry

Activity: _____ **Teacher**: Take T6 and place a mirror along one of its sides. Place a block behind the mirror so that it is in the same position as the image. Remove the mirror and outline the shape you have made. Be sure to draw a line where the mirror was. Do this for each one of the sides of T6. What can you say about what happened?
Student: Sometimes you get a triangle, sometimes you don't.
Teacher: Do this for other shapes. Write about the differences and similarities of the reflections you create.

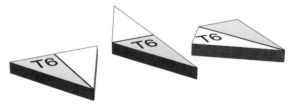

Questions to explore with students:

- Reflect a parallelogram over each side. Draw a dotted line that connects corresponding vertices (the end points of corresponding angles). Measure the distance from each vertex to the line of reflection. What is true about these distances? Do the same for other shapes.

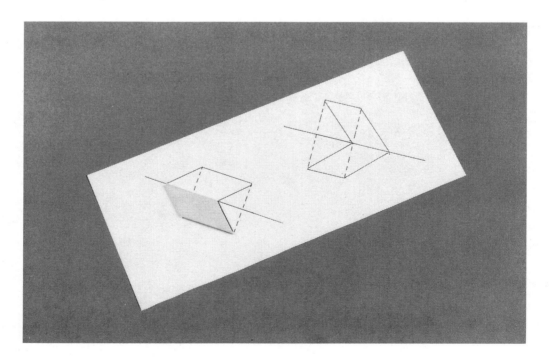

SIMILAR POWER BLOCKS

Materials: _____ Power Blocks
Unlined paper

Purpose: _____ To identify similar geometric shapes among the Power Blocks

Activity: _____ **Teacher**: We are going to search for similar geometric shapes among the Power Blocks. Place T5 flat on your desk. Hold T3 in your hand and stand in front of T5. Hold T3 so it is just above T5. Align two sides and an angle of T3 with those of T5. You have to get your head right over the top of the triangles. Close one eye. Slowly bring T3 toward your other eye. At the same time you are doing this, you must keep the sides and angle of the two triangles aligned. What happens to T5 as you do this?
Student: As you bring T3 up, it covers more and more of T5.
Teacher: Is there ever a point when T3 appears to be congruent with T5?
Student: I don't understand.
Teacher: Is there ever a point when T3 appears to cover T5 exactly with nothing left to cover and nothing hanging over?
Student: Yes.
Teacher: If it appears to be congruent, then the two shapes are similar. Are there other Power Block shapes that are similar to each other?

When students understand how to do this, they make a record of what they have found by tracing the two shapes and noting whether they are similar or not.

Questions to explore with students:

– Did you find any shapes that were similar to more than one shape? If so, can you put them in an order that illustrates their similarity?
– Are all the triangles similar?
– Are all the rectangles similar?
– If you found a series of shapes that were similar, can you make the next shape in the series by putting Power Blocks together?

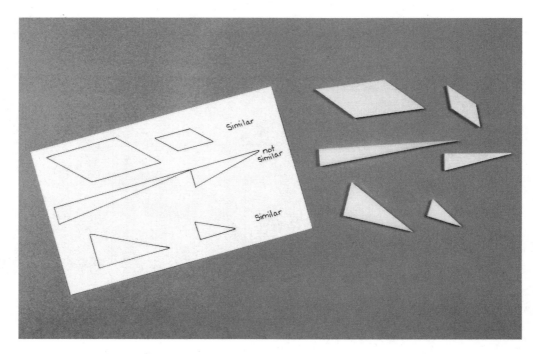

SIMILAR SHAPES

Materials: _____ Power Blocks
Unlined paper
Clear vinyl 8 X 11 x 20 mils thick

Purpose: _____ To build similar geometric shapes with Power Blocks

Activity: _____ **Teacher**: Make this shape using T2, S3 and R2

Can you make another shape similar to the one I have just made?
Student: Yes.
Teacher: What blocks did you use?
Student: T3, S4, and R4.
Teacher: Take T2, S3, and R2 and build the shape on a sheet of vinyl. Hold the shape on the vinyl over the shape you just made with T2, T3, and R2 and check to see if it is similar to the first shape. Is it?
Student: No.
Teacher: What could you do to make it similar? Can you make another shape that is similar to the first?

When students understand how to do this, they make a record of what they have found by tracing the shapes on a piece of paper. They may stack their tracings in order of increasing size and staple them together.

Questions to explore with students:

- How far were you able to extend your series of similar shapes?
- If you could make a series of shapes using two blocks at each step, could you do a series using three blocks at each step?
- How many T1s did it take to make each of your shapes? Is there a pattern that would enable you to predict the number of T1s for any step in the series of shapes?

SIMILAR POWER BLOCKS

Materials: _____
Power Blocks
Protractors
Rulers
Calculators
Lined paper

Purpose: _____ To explore the properties of sides of similar shapes

Activity: _____ Each group of students needs to have families of power blocks they have identified as similar, for example: T1, T2, T3, T4, T5.

Teacher: The vertex of an angle is the point where the lines that form its sides meet. Label the vertices of the triangles A, B and C. make C the vertex of the right angle. I want you to make a table like this:

Shape	Side AC	Ratio	Side BC	Ratio	Side AB (hypt.)	Ratio

Take T1 and measure its sides in millimeters. Record your measurements in the table like this:

Shape	Side AC	Ratio	Side BC	Ratio	Side AB (hypt.)	Ratio
T1	25		25		35	

Take T2 and measure its sides. Record its measurements in the Table like this:

Shape	Side AC	Ratio	Side BC	Ratio	Side AB (hypt.)	Ratio
T1	25		25		35	
T2	35		35		50	

Use your calculator to determine the ratio of the sides of T2 to corresponding sides of T1. How much is 35 divided by 25?

Student: About 1.4

Teacher: T2s side is 1.4 times longer than T1s. Do this for each of the other sides and I will record your data...Here is what you came up with:

Shape	Side AC	Ratio	Side BC	Ratio	Side AB (hypt.)	Ratio
T1	25		25		35	
T2	35	1.4	35	1.4	50	1.4

Do you see a pattern with respect to how the sides of T2 grew with respect to T1?

Student: They are about the same.

Teacher: What does it mean if they are the same?

Student: Each side of the larger triangle is 1.4 times larger than the smaller triangle.

Teacher: Measure the corresponding angles with a protractor. What did you find out?

Student: They are equal.

Teacher: Explore the relationship between the corresponding sides of two other similar shapes. Record your data in a table like the one above. Measure the corresponding angles. Do you see a pattern? Can you write a definition for similar shapes?

Questions to explore with students:

– What would happen if you traced a shape on top of a similar shape so that they have one corresponding angle in common? Continue to do this for each shape in the family of similar shapes. What can you say about similar shapes based on this drawing?

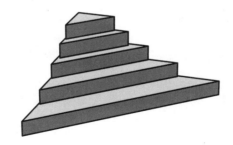

TANGRAMS

Materials: _____ Power Blocks
Student made tangram puzzle
Clear vinyl sheet 8 X 11 20 mills thick

Purpose: _____ To create tangram puzzles from Power Blocks

Activity: _____ The activity that follows should be preceded by the following lessons from *Mathematics...A Way Of Thinking*: Lesson 20 – 1, Tangram Puzzle, in which students fold and tear a square of paper to create their own puzzle. Lesson 20 – 2, Tangram Puzzle, which provides practice at assembling tangram pieces into specific shapes.

There are four standard metric tangrams in every set of Power Blocks. This tangram set is made from two T4s, one T3, two T2s, one S2, and one P2. There are other sets of tangrams that can be made with Power Blocks.

Teacher: You have created your own tangram puzzles from squares of paper. Can you make a tangram puzzle from the pieces in your set of Power Blocks?
Student: Yes. Mine is a different size than other peoples.
Teacher: I wonder how many different size tangram puzzles are in your set of Power Blocks?

Questions to explore with students:

– Were the different size tangram puzzles similar? Use a piece of vinyl to check your shapes.
– If you can tape blocks together, what is the largest tangram puzzle you can make with a set of Power Blocks?

TANGRAMS

Materials: _____ Power Blocks
Tangram triangle paper

Purpose: _____ To create tangram puzzles from Power Blocks

Activity: _____ Power Blocks may be used for tangram Lesson 20 – 3 in *Mathematics…a Way of Thinking*. The tangram triangle paper in *Mathematics a Way of Thinking* is made for tangram puzzles 4 X 4 inches. Power Blocks are cut to metric units. The tangram triangle blackline provided in this book is made for a square that is 100 X 100 millimeters. The difference between the two is very slight, but may cause problems for some students. It is best to use paper that matches the units of the tangram puzzle students are using. Use tangram sets made from two T4s, one T3, two T2s, one S2, and one P2 when using the triangle paper provided in this book.

You might want to read to your students *Grandfather Tang's Story* by Ann Tompert[1] to your students to motivate them. The story relates to the use of tangrams to create designs that may be made with tangrams.

[1]Tompert, Ann. Grandfather Tang's Story. New York, NY: Crown Publishers, Inc.

PYTHAGOREAN RELATIONSHIPS

Materials: _____ Power Blocks
Unlined paper
Calculators

Purpose: _____ To investigate the Pythagorean relationship of the sides of right triangles

Activity: _____ **Teacher**: We are going to explore the relationship of the sides of right triangles. The side opposite the right angle is called the hypotenuse. Take out T1. See if you can surround it with squares that have sides exactly the same length as the sides of the triangle. Here is an example of what I mean.

Can you find squares to put against the other sides?
Student: Yes.
Teacher: What blocks did you use?
Student: I used 2 S1s and S2.

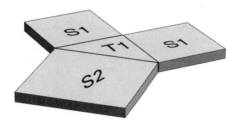

Teacher: If S1 is one square unit of area, can you use T1s to determine the area of S2?
Student: Two square units
Teacher: I want you to record your information like this. Find all the different triangles you can find in the set of blocks that you can surround with squares. Call the smaller squares A and B, and the large square C. Record their areas.

Triangle	Square A	Square B	Square C
T1	1	1	2
T2	2	2	4
T3			

If you knew the area of square A and square B, could you predict the area of Square C?

Questions to explore with students:

- If you know the area of a square, how could you use your calculator to determine the length of its side?
- Which triangles in the set do not have a square that is the same length as their hypotenuse?
- If you knew the area of the square that was needed to match the hypotenuse of a block, could you use your calculator to determine the length of the hypotenuse?
- For those triangles in the set of blocks that do not have a square the same length as their hypotenuse, could you determine what size square you would need to add to the set?
- Do you see a pattern that would enable you to predict the length of the hypotenuse of any right triangle?

MEASUREMENT

In this chapter students measure the attributes of length, area, mass, and angle.

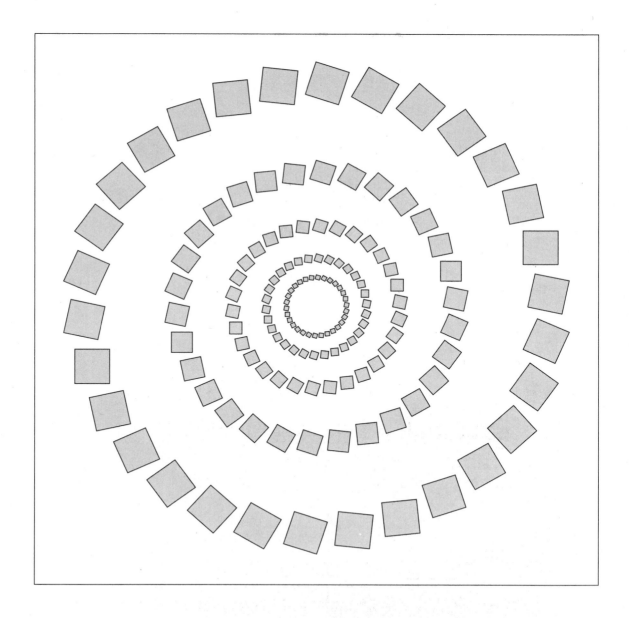

LENGTH: NONSTANDARD UNITS

Materials: _____ Power Blocks
Unlined paper

Purpose: _____ To measure length using S1 blocks

Activity: _____ **Teacher:** I have just made this train of S1 blocks. How many S1s did I use?

Student: Eight.
Teacher: Okay. The train is eight S1s long. I have made another train. How many blocks did I use to make this train?
Student: Seven

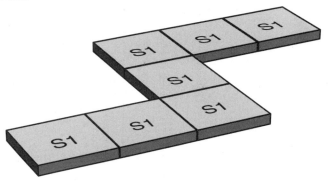

Teacher: Right. So we can say the train is seven blocks long. Please make your own trains now. Use no more than two handfuls of S1s to make each train. The blocks must be connected so we can imagine your blocks as a train. Record the length of your train on a piece of paper and place it beside your train.

When students can measure the length of their trains in terms of S1 blocks, they may use the S1 blocks to measure other objects in the room.

Teacher: I want you to work with a partner. One person on each team get a book and put it in front of your partner. Together, estimate how many S1 blocks long your book is. Take out that number of S1s. Record your estimate. Try to make your estimate within plus or minus one block of the actual measurement. Now measure the length of the book using S1s and record your measurement. Was your estimate greater than, less than, or equal to your measurement?
Student: Greater.
Teacher: Was it within plus or minus one block of the measurement? Use symbols or words to record this information.

When students understand what is required, they work together estimating the length of objects found in the room. After making their estimates, they measure the length of the objects with S1 blocks. They record the results and compare the estimated length with the measured length.

Questions to explore with students:

- What would happen if we changed the S1 block to a larger block?
- What would happen if we changed the S1 block to a smaller block?
- Would the measurement change?
- If the measurements changed, how would they change?

LENGTH: PERIMETER NONSTANDARD UNITS

Materials: _____ Power Blocks
Unlined paper

Purpose: _____ To measure perimeter using S1s

Activity: _____ **Teacher:** Take out an S1. I am going to say the side of S1 is one unit long. How many sides does S1 have?
Student: Four.
Teacher: The sum of the lengths of the sides of a shape is its perimeter. What is the sum of the lengths of the sides of S1?
Student: Four.
Teacher: Yes. The perimeter of S1 is four. Take out two S1s. Put them together so they make one shape. When you put them together, their sides and corners must line up. What shape did you get?
Student: A rectangle
Teacher: Did anyone get a different shape?
Student: I don't see any.
Teacher: Okay. What is the perimeter of your shape?
Student: Six.
Teacher: How many different shapes can you make using three S1s? Make sure the sides and corners line up. Don't make shapes that just have the corners of the pieces touching.
Student: I made two different shapes.
Teacher: How long are their perimeters?
Student: Eight S1s long.
Teacher: Take out four S1s and make as many different shapes as you can using four S1s. Record the perimeter of each shape on a piece of paper.

When students understand what is required, they work together to explore the perimeters possible for a given number of S1s. They may make a record of their work by tracing their shapes and recording their perimeters on a piece of paper.

Questions to explore with students:

- Is there more than one way to make a shape with the same perimeter?
- Do you see a pattern that would help you predict the longest perimeter for a given number of S1s?
- Do you see a pattern that would help you predict the shortest perimeter for a given number of S1s?
- Is there a pattern that would enable you to predict the number of different perimeters that are possible for a given number of S1s?

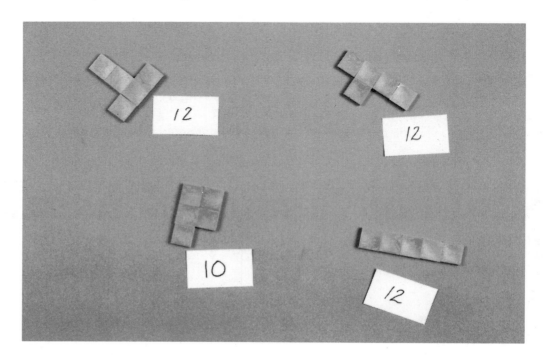

LENGTH: PERIMETER STANDARD UNITS

Materials: _____ Power Blocks
Unlined paper
Centimeter cubes

Purpose: _____ To develop a sense of the magnitude of a metric unit by measuring the perimeter of the blocks
with centimeter cubes

Activity: _____ **Teacher:** Today we are going to measure the perimeters of the blocks with centimeter cubes.
The length of each side of a cube is one centimeter. Take out S5. How many sides does S5 have?
Student: Four.
Teacher: Put out the number of centimeter cubes you think it would take to go around the
outside of the block. Try to make your estimate come within a range of plus or minus four cubes
of the measured perimeter. Snap them together.
Student: Okay. My estimate is thirty- two centimeters.
Teacher: Use a different set of cubes to measure the length of each side of S5. When you have
finished, snap the cubes together. How did your estimate compare to your measurement? Was it
within the range of plus or minus four cubes?
Student: It was eight cubes too short.
Teacher: Make a tracing of S5 and record your estimate and your measurement. You may record
the information like this:

Estimate	Comparison	Measurement
32	is less than	40

Or you may write it like this using symbols:

Estimate	Comparison	Measurement
32	<	40

Students estimate the perimeters of other blocks by setting out the number of cubes they think
are equal to the perimeter. They surround the block and count the total number of cubes used.
They compare the two numbers and describe the relationship between them with words or
symbols. The results of their measurements for a given block will vary. Some of the sides of the
shapes are not evenly divisible by cubes. The cubes will be a little too short or a little too long to
exactly match the length of a side. Students will vary their approach to solving this problem. The
issue is how close is close enough. It is important to discuss it because it is a problem common
to all measurements.

When students can measure the perimeter of a single block with cubes, they make polygons
using several blocks. When making polygons, it is easier for students to trace the shape first,
then measure it. After they have traced their polygon, they record their estimate of the perimeter. They measure the perimeter, record their results, and compare the measured results with
the estimate. They may pass their tracing to a neighbor who re-measures the polygon to confirm
the perimeter.

Questions to explore with students:

- How close were your estimates of a block's perimeter to the measured length? Were they within an acceptable range?
- How close do you think they should be? What is close enough?
- Can you sort your blocks based on their perimeters?

AREA: NONSTANDARD UNITS

Materials: _____ Power Blocks
Unlined paper

Purpose: _____ To measure the area of squares and rectangles using S1s

Activity: _____ **Teacher:** Take out R5. We are going to measure its area. A block's area is the number of square units it takes to cover it. Estimate how many S1s it would take to cover R5. Try to estimate within plus or minus one S1 of the actual area. What did you estimate?
Student: Twenty-five.
Teacher: Measure the area of R5 by covering it with S1s. How many S1s did it take to cover R5?
Student: Sixteen.
Teacher: Okay. We say that R5 has an area of 16 square units. I want you to work with a partner to measure the areas of the squares and rectangles in your set of blocks. Try to make your estimates fall within two blocks of the measured area.

When students have measured the area for all the squares and rectangles in their set of blocks, they may make additional squares and rectangles by putting together combinations of blocks. In each case, they trace the perimeter of the shape they have created. They do not draw the internal structure. They estimate its area. Then they measure its area with S1s. Finally, they compare their estimated area with the measured area.

Teacher: Make a table with three columns. Label the columns like this:

Length   Width   Area

If S1 is one square unit of area and the length of its sides are one unit of length, measure the length and width of the rectangles and squares you have covered. I have collected some of your data. Here is how I want you to record the information:

Length	Width	Area
1	1	1
8	2	16
4	4	16
2	4	8

As you record the information see, if you can see a pattern that would help you predict the area of a square or rectangle if you knew its length and width.

Questions to explore with students:

– What is the area of your paper, desk, favorite book, or a friend's favorite book?
– Could you predict the area of a rectangular or square object without using S1s to cover it?

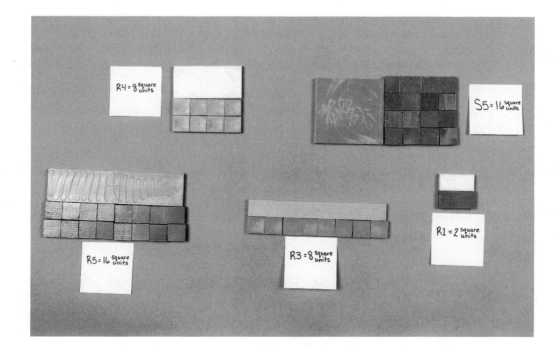

AREA: NONSTANDARD UNITS

Materials: _____ Power Blocks
Table of Relative Areas (blackline master)
Unlined paper
Calculators

Purpose: _____ To record the area of the blocks systematically
To use this information to measure the area of student generated shapes

Activity: _____ **Teacher:** Take out as many T1s as you can find in the next two minutes. How many T1s does it take to cover an S1?
Student: Two.
Teacher: Okay. Two T1s cover an S1. If T1 is equal to one square unit of area, what is the area of S1?
Student: Two square units.
Teacher: Record this information in your Table of Relative Areas. Next to T1, write the number 1, and next to the S1 write the number 2.
Student: Okay.
Teacher: I'm going to say T1 is one unit of area. How many T1s does it take to cover T2?
Student: Two.
Teacher: What is the area of T2?
Student: Two square units.
Teacher: Record it in your table next to T2. Please find out how many T1s cover each of the other blocks. Record your answers in your table.

When the class has completed this task and agrees on the relative area of each block, they are ready to generate their own area task cards.

Teacher: Take out three blocks. Put them together to make a polygon.
Student: Which blocks?
Teacher: Any three blocks you want.
Student: How do you want them to go together?
Teacher: It does not matter as long as their sides are touching and they form a polygon. When you have finished making your shape, trace it. When you trace it, only show its perimeter. Do not show how the shape is made. When you finish, make another polygon using three blocks.
Student: How many shapes do we draw? May we color them?
Teacher: Make as many as you can in the next fifteen minutes. Yes, you may color them. When you are finished I will collect your work.

The teacher chooses an example of a student-generated task card to demonstrate to the class.

Teacher: If T1 is equal to one square unit area, what do you estimate the area of this shape to be?
Student: (Number is volunteered.)
Teacher: How could we measure its area?
Student: Put T1s on it until it is covered. Then count them.
Teacher: I don't think I have enough T1s to cover the shape. How can I measure it?
Student: We know the area of other bigger pieces. Put bigger pieces on first. Use the T1s after all the space has been filled in.
Teacher: Okay. I can put a S4 here and a P3 here. Now what do I do?
Student: Put two T1s in the space that is left.
Teacher: Okay. Now it is covered. How do I find the area of the polygon?

Student: Add them up. S4 equals 16. P3 equals 8, and two T1s equal 2. When I added them, I got 26.

Teacher: How did your measurement compare to your estimate?

When students understand the process of measuring the area of the polygons, the teacher passes out the rest of the cards to the class. Students work together to measure the area of polygons. They first make an estimate of the area of their shape and record it on the task card. Next, they measure the shape with blocks and record their results on the task card. They compare their estimate with the measured area.

Questions to explore with students:

- Did you use a strategy to measure the area of your shape?
- What strategy did you use?
- Were any shapes impossible to measure? If so, why?

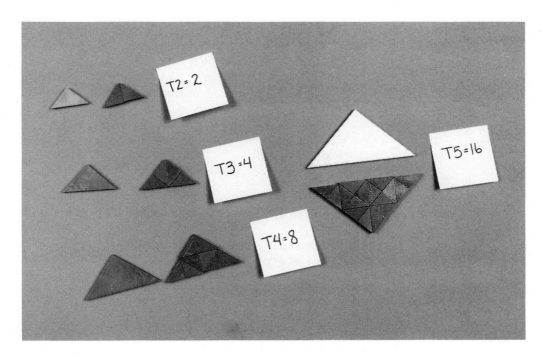

AREA: STANDARD UNITS

Materials: _____ Power Blocks
Table of Relative Areas (blackline master)
Centimeter grid paper (blackline master)
Calculators

Purpose: _____ To develop a sense of the magnitude of a metric unit by measuring the area of the blocks using centimeter grid paper

Activity: _____ **Teacher:** Take out T1. Estimate the number of square centimeters it would take to cover the T1. Write it down.
Student: (Assorted numbers are volunteered.)
Teacher: Now place T1 on your grid paper and trace around it. How many square centimeters does it cover?
Student: Three and a little bit more.
Teacher: Estimate how much the little bit is and record your result on your drawing. Compare your estimate with your measurement. Measure the area of the other blocks using centimeter grid paper.

To do the following, the class must have been taught how to find an average. When the class has measured the area of each block, the teacher collects the data and consolidates it. She/he shows the class a list of all the areas for a given shape.

Teacher: When the class measured the area of P3, it got a range of different areas. Here is a list of your data. Find the average area of P3 and record it in a Table of Relative Areas.

When the students understand what they are to do, the teacher lists the class results for the other blocks. They determine the average area for each of the blocks and record it in a Table of Relative Areas. The teacher saves the averages so they can be compared to the data in the next lesson.

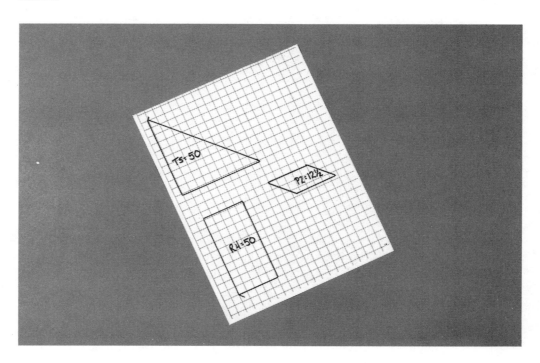

AREA: STANDARD UNITS

Materials: _____ Power Blocks
Table of Relative Areas (blackline master)
Calculators
Metric rulers graduated in millimeters

Purpose: _____ To develop a sense of the magnitude of a metric unit by measuring the length of the sides of the blocks using a ruler

Activity: _____ To do the activity that follows, students need to be able to measure with a metric ruler and be familiar with the formulas for the areas of squares, rectangles, parallelograms, and triangles.

Teacher: I want you to work in groups of two or three. Take out T3. Measure the base to the nearest millimeter.
Student: Which side is the base?
Teacher: Stand your triangle up so a side with the right angle is resting on the desktop. We will call that side the base. Record your measurement.
Student: Okay.
Teacher: Now measure the height to the nearest millimeter. Let's call the height the other side of the right angle.
Student: Okay.
Teacher: Remember the formula for the area of a triangle A=1/2 bh. Calculate the area of T3 based on your measurements. Write the area of T3 in a Table of Relative Areas.
Student: Okay.
Teacher: Calculate the area of each of the other triangles using the formula. Write the results in a Table of Relative Areas.

The process is repeated for the other shapes. Each shape is measured, the measurement plugged into the appropriate formula, and the area calculated.

Teacher: When the class calculated the area of T3, it came up with different answers. Here they are. What is the average of these areas?
Student: Calculate the average.
Teacher: Take out the Table of Relative Areas from yesterday's lesson. Write the average area of T3 beside yesterday's answer.

When the students understand what they are to do, they determine the average area of each of the blocks. They record it in the table with the average measurements from the previous lesson.

Questions to explore with students:

– Were any of the results of your measurements with graph paper the same as those with the ruler? Which one(s)?

– Which method of determining the area of the blocks was more accurate, the graph paper or the ruler? Why?

– Which method of determining area do you think would be the most useful outside a classroom?

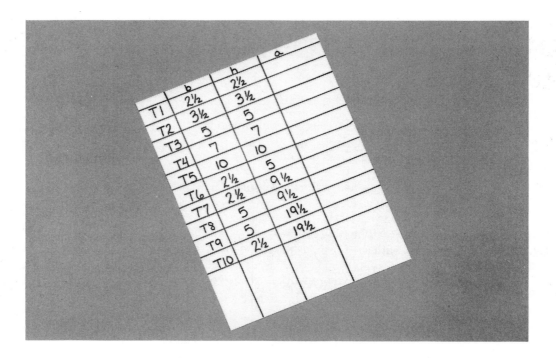

	b	a	
T1	2½	2½	
T2	3½	3½	
T3	5	5	
T4	7	7	
T5	10	10	
T6	2½	5	
T7	2½	9½	
T8	5	9½	
T9	5	19½	
T10	2½	19½	

AREA: STANDARD UNITS

Materials: _____ Power Blocks
Calculators
Unlined paper

Purpose: _____ To determine the area of Power Blocks by logical thinking

Activity: _____ **Teacher:** Today we are going to see if we can determine the area of the blocks by doing as little measuring as possible. When we used the centimeter graph paper, you said the area of S5 was 100 square centimeters. When we measured S5 with a ruler, you said that it was 10 x 10 centimeters and had an area of 100 square centimeters. Let's see if we can use that information to figure out the other areas. How many R4s does it take to make S5?
Student: Two.
Teacher: What fraction of S5 is R4?
Student: One-half.
Teacher: So R4 is half of S5. If S5 is 100 square centimeters, what is the area of R4?
Student: Fifty square centimeters.

Student determine the area of each piece based on S5 being 100 square centimeters. They record the information with the data from the previous two methods.

Questions to explore with students:

– Were any of the results of your measurements with graph paper and the ruler the same as those we determined by logical thinking? Which one(s)?

– Which method of determining the areas of the blocks was more accurate? Why?

– Is the third method useful outside the classroom?

SURFACE AREA OF SOLIDS: STANDARD UNITS

Materials: _____ Power Blocks
Centimeter grid paper
Calculators
Cellophane tape or masking tape
Small gummed labels (removable)
Scissors

Purpose: _____ To measure the surface area of a solid

Activity: _____ Prior to the lesson, students choose three identical blocks and stack the blocks on top of one another. When they have made enough stacks, they tape each stack of three blocks together to make a solid. They stick a gummed label on each surface of the solid and number the surfaces by writing on each label. The purpose is to make sets of solid shapes for use in the next lesson.

Teacher: Here is a stack of three S5s that have been taped together. Number each surface. How many surfaces does the shape have?
Student: Six.
Teacher: Place S5 on top of a piece of centimeter grid paper. Trace this surface of the solid. Flip it ninety degrees, and trace the new surface. Continue this for each surface. As you trace each surface, write the surface's number on the tracing. When you have finished tracing each surface of the shape, you should be able to be cut it out as a single piece of paper.
Student: I can't make it come out that way.
Teacher: It is difficult. After you trace a surface, flip it ninety degrees. Keep doing that until all the surfaces have been traced.
Student: Okay.
Teacher: Cut it out.
Student: Okay.
Teacher: Can you make a "jacket" for the solid with the piece of paper you have just cut out? It should fit the solid as snugly as possible. Use tape to hold it in place.
Student: It's not very snug.
Teacher: It looks close enough. How could you measure the surface area of this solid?
Student: Count the squares.
Teacher: Which squares?
Student: All the squares on the "jacket".
Teacher: Okay. Let's do that.
Students: Provide different answers.
Teacher: When the class measured the surface area of S5, these are the results. Calculate the average area for S5.

When students understand what they are to measure, they work together to measure the surface areas of other solids. The measurements are shared and an average calculated for each solid.

Questions to explore with students:

- Is it possible to use formulas to calculate the surface areas of the solids?
- What formulas would you use?
- Compare the results of the measurements made with "jackets" to those calculated using formulas.

MASS: NONSTANDARD UNITS

Materials: _____ Power Blocks
Balance
Common objects

Purpose: _____ To measure the mass of objects in the classroom using S1 as the unit of measure

Activity: _____ **Teacher:** Today we are going to measure the mass of this eraser. Estimate its mass. (Teacher demonstrates adding S1s to one side of a balance until it is balanced.) What is the mass of the eraser?
Student: Students count S1s.
Teacher: I have collected common objects for you to measure. Measure each object and record the results of your measurements.

Questions to explore with students:

– How could you measure the mass of an object if it was heavier than all your S1s put together?
– What is the mass of each Power Block if S1 has a mass of one?

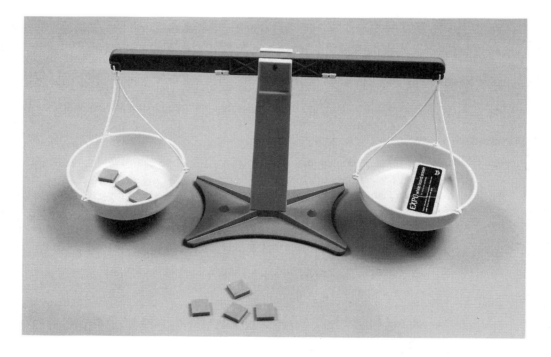

MASS: 1, 2, 4, 8, 16...

Materials: _____ Power Blocks
Balance(s)
Lined paper
Common objects
Gummed labels (removable)

Purpose: _____ To measure the mass of objects using T1, T2, T3, T4, and T5

Activity: _____ Prior to the lesson, the teacher needs to make sets of blocks consisting of T1, T2, T3, T4, and T5. One set is required for each balance. A gummed label needs to be placed on each side of each blocks.

Teacher: If T1 is equal to one unit of mass, how could you find the mass of T2?
Student: Weigh it with T1s.
Teacher: When you do that, what is the mass of T2?
Student: Two T1s.
Teacher: Okay. Write 2 on the gummed labels on T2, and 1 on the labels on T1.
Student: Okay.
Teacher: What is the mass of each of the other blocks?
Student: T3 is four. T4 is eight and T5 is sixteen.
Teacher: Record the block's mass on the label. Take a piece of paper and draw vertical lines on it to make seven columns. The second column from the left should be a little wider than the others.
Student: Okay.
Teacher: At the top of the third column from the left, write T5. In the fourth column write T4, in the next write T3, then T2, and finally T1. Write the numbers from one to thirty-one in the left hand column. Write one number on each line starting with the second line.
Student: Got it.
Teacher: I want you to measure the mass of objects found in the room. Use only the five triangles with the gummed labels.
Student: Can we mix sets to get more pieces?
Teacher: No. What is the mass of this ruler? If I put T1 on the other side of the balance, nothing happens. If I add T2, nothing happens. If I add T3, the balance is now out of balance in the other direction. What can I do to make it balance?
Student: Take out T1.
Teacher: Okay. Now it is balanced. T2 has a mass of 2. T3 has a mass of 4. What is the mass of the ruler?
Student: Six.
Teacher: Next to the number six on your record sheet, write the word "ruler". How many T5s did I use?
Student: None.
Teacher: Write 0 in the T5 column next to the word ruler. How many T4s did I use?
Student: None.
Teacher: Write zero in the T4 column next to the other zero. How many T3s did I use?
Student: One.
Teacher: Write one in the T3 column. How many T2s did I use?
Student: One.
Teacher: Write one in the T2 column. How many T1s did I use?
Student: Zero.
Teacher: Write zero in the T1 column. Measure the mass of other objects found in the room. When you record your results, what is the largest number you will ever have to write in a column?
Student: One.

Teacher: What is the smallest?
Student: Zero.

Questions to explore with students:

- Were there any whole numbers between one and thirty-one that you could not make with the five blocks? Which ones?

- Look at the matrix we have made. Do you see a pattern going down any of the columns?

- What base uses only ones and zeros to record quantities?

- We used blocks with masses of 1, 2, 4 ,8, and 16. If we wanted to add to our collection, what would the mass of the next block have to be to keep the pattern going?

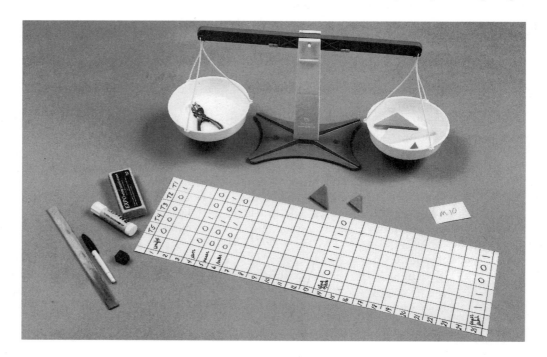

MEASURING ANGLES

Materials: _____ Power Blocks
Transparent protractors (blackline master)

Purpose: _____ To measure the interior angles of Power Blocks

Activity: _____ Each team of students needs a transparent protractor. These can be made by using the blackline at the back of the book to make overhead projector transparencies.

Teacher: Today we are going to measure angles. How many sections are there in your protractor?

Student: Seventy-two.

Teacher: How many degrees are there in a circle?

Student: Three-hundred-sixty.

Teacher: How many degrees are set off by each section of your protractor?

Student: Five.

Teacher: Take out T5. To measure an interior angle of T5, place the dot at the center of the protractor on the vertex of one of the angles. Line up one side of T5 with any line on the protractor. Count each section of the protractor as five degrees. Count until you reach the other side of the triangle. How many degrees are there in each of the angles of T5?

Student: Forty-five, forty-five, and ninety.

Teacher: Make a record by tracing T5 and recording your results on your drawing. Measure the interior angles of each of the other blocks.

Questions to explore with students:

- Measure the exterior angles of the shapes. Do you see a pattern that would enable you to predict the exterior angle of a shape if you knew the interior angle?

- Do you see a pattern that would enable you to predict the sum of the angles of a block?

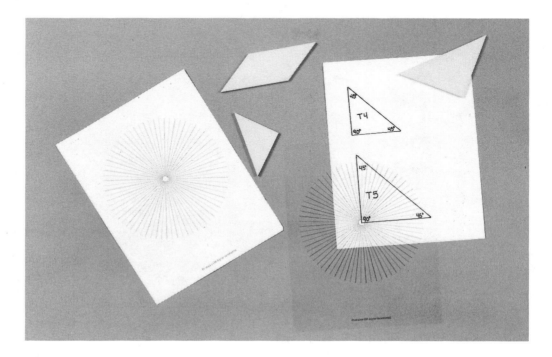

MEASURING ANGLES

Materials: _____ Power Blocks
Transparent protractors
Calculators

Purpose: _____ To measure the interior angles of student generated polygons

Activity: _____ **Teacher:** Today I want you to make polygons using several Power Blocks. I have made one using two S5s, one P4, and one T9. Make the same shape. Trace it and measure its interior angles.
Student: Okay.
Teacher: How many degrees in each of the angles?
Student: 105, 90, 90, 225, 135, 45, 225, and 165.
Teacher: What is the sum of the interior angles?
Student: 1080.
Teacher: How many sides did it have?
Student: Eight.
Teacher: Make a two column table. Label one column "number of sides". Label the other column "sum of angles". Make as many polygons as you can. Measure the interior angles of each polygon, and calculate their sum. Count its sides and record your information in your table.

Questions to explore with students:

− Do all shapes with the same number of sides have the same sum for the interior angles?
− Do you see a pattern that would help you predict the sum of the interior angles if you knew the number of sides?

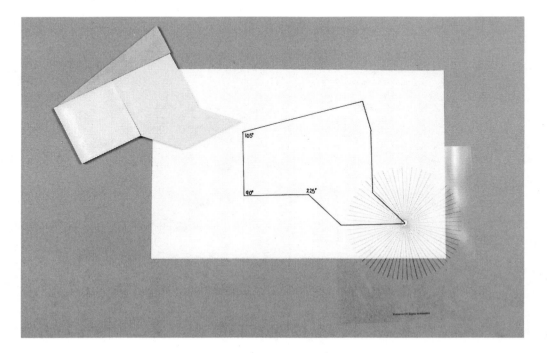

FRACTIONS

The activities that follow are organized roughly in order of difficulty. However, they may be used in the order you determine is best. The lessons are not intended to be an exhaustive study of the subject of teaching fractions. Rather, they are intended to demonstrate the range of possibilities that Power Blocks bring to the subject.

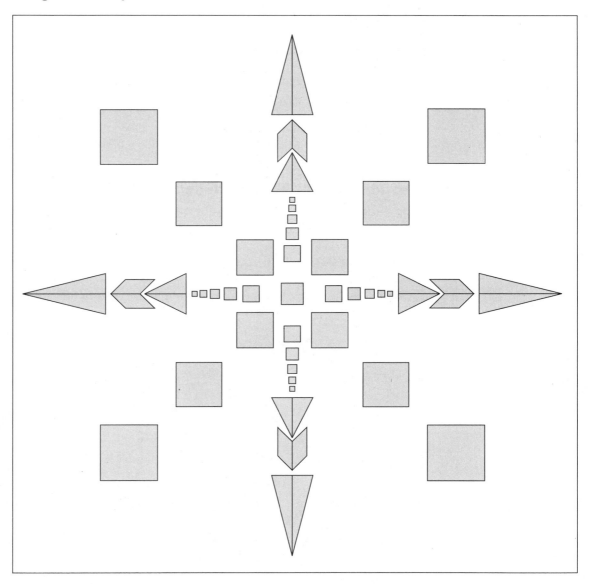

IDENTIFYING FRACTIONAL VALUES

Materials: _____ Power Blocks
Unlined paper
Yarn loops

Purpose: _____ To identify the fractional values within a mixed group of blocks

Activity: _____ Teacher takes about six blocks at random, and places the blocks in a yarn loop.

Teacher: How many blocks are there in the loop?
Student: Six.
Teacher: How many of the blocks are S2s?
Student: Two.
Teacher: Six blocks altogether and two of the blocks are S2s. What fraction of the blocks are S2s?
Student: Two-sixths.
Teacher: Let's make a label. What fraction are P2s?
Student: Two-sixths.
Teacher: What fraction of the blocks are...

When students understand what is required, they work in pairs placing a number of blocks inside a yarn loop (limit the number of blocks to those that can be held in two hands). They label their work with slips of paper. Students may make a record of their work by tracing what they have done.

Questions to explore with students:

– How many sixths are there in your group of blocks?
– If you had seven blocks in your group, how many sevenths did it take to make your group of blocks?
– If you had five blocks in your group, how many fifths did it take to make your group of blocks?
– Do you see a pattern that would enable you to predict the number of fractional parts it takes to make one whole group?

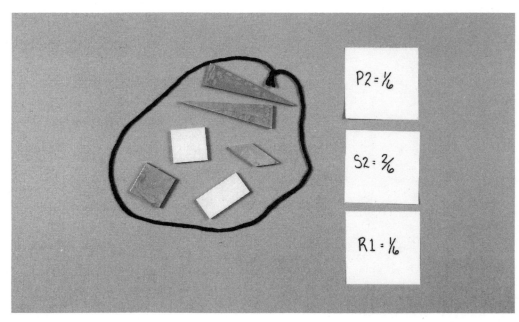

IDENTIFYING FRACTIONAL VALUES

Materials: _____ Power Blocks
Unlined paper

Purpose: _____ To assign fractional values to specific Power Blocks

Activity: _____ **Teacher**: Take out S5. S5 is one square unit of area. Are there two identical blocks that can exactly cover S5?
Student: Yes. Two R4s.
Teacher: Is there another way to cover S5 with two blocks?
Student: Yes. Two T5s.
Teacher: What fraction of S5 is R4?
Student: One-half.
Teacher: What fraction of S5 is T5?
Student: One-half.
Teacher: Pick any other block, and see how many different ways you can cover it with two identical blocks.

When students understand what is required, they may choose any block and investigate ways to cover it with four identical blocks. As students continue their explorations of ways to cover a larger block with smaller blocks that are identical, they may make a recording of their work by tracing the blocks. The drawings show how the smaller blocks cover the larger block. Students assign fractional values to the blocks covering the bottom block which is defined as one square unit of area.

Questions to explore with students:

– If T4 is one fourth, how many fourths make a one square unit of area?

– If R4 equals one square unit of area, how many halves did it take to cover it? How many fourths? How many eighths? How many sixteenths? If you knew the fractional value of one covering block, do you see a pattern that would help you predict the number of blocks it would take to cover R4?

– If you had blocks that were thirds, fifths, or sixths, could you predict how many it would take to cover one square unit of area?

NONCONGRUENT WHOLE UNITS OF AREA

Materials: _____ Power Blocks
Unlined paper

Purpose: _____ To make different shapes that have one square unit of area

Activity: _____ **Teacher**: If T3 is one-half square unit of area, how would you make a shape that is one square unit of area?
Student: Use two T3s.
Teacher: See how many different ways you can make one square unit of area using T3s. Make sure the sides of the blocks are touching.

The teacher changes the definition of one-half square unit of area. Students repeat the activity until they are comfortable with the idea that shapes can have the same area and not look alike.

Teacher: If P4 is one-fourth of a square unit of area, see how many ways you can make shapes with one square unit of area.
Student: Can we use other blocks?
Teacher: What do you mean?
Student: Some blocks have the same area as P4, but are different shapes. Can we use them?
Teacher: Yes, as long as they are the same area as P4.

When students understand what is required, they may define any block in terms of a fraction with a numerator of one. They then see how many different ways they can make shapes of one square unit of area. They may make a record of what they have done by tracing their work.

Questions to explore with students:

– Can different shapes have the same area?
– Is there a limit to the number of ways you can make shapes with the same area?

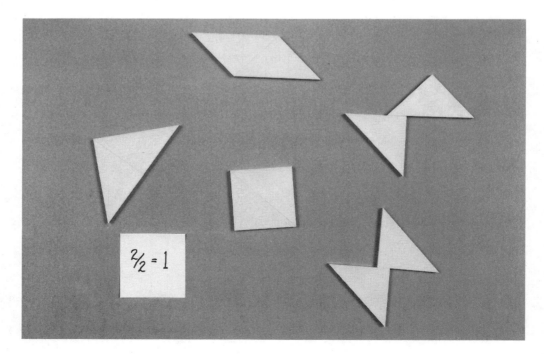

ASSIGNING RELATIVE FRACTIONAL VALUES

Materials: _____ Power Blocks
Unlined paper
Table of Relative Areas (blackline master)

Purpose: _____ To assign relative fractional values to the blocks

Activity: _____ **Teacher:** Take out S5. Trace it on a piece of paper. S5 is one square unit of area. How many T3s does it take to exactly cover S5?
Student: Four.
Teacher: Correct. What fraction of S5 is T4?
Student: One-fourth.
Teacher: Make a tracing that shows how four T4s make S5, and record the fractional value of each T3 on your tracing. If S5 is one square unit of area, how much is T3?
Student: One eighth.
Teacher: See if you can determine the area of each of the different blocks.

Students may record their results by making tracings and writing the fractional values in a Table of Relative Areas. When they have determined the areas of the various blocks, change the definition of one square unit of area and repeat the process. One square unit of area can be defined in terms of any block or combination of blocks.

Questions to explore with students:

– If P3 equals one, what are the areas of the other blocks?
– If R4 equals one, what are the areas of the other blocks?
– If S5 equals 1/3, what are the areas of the other blocks?
– If S3 equals 3/7, what are the areas of the other blocks?
– Do you see a pattern that would help you predict what a block's area would be once you decide the area of one of the other blocks?

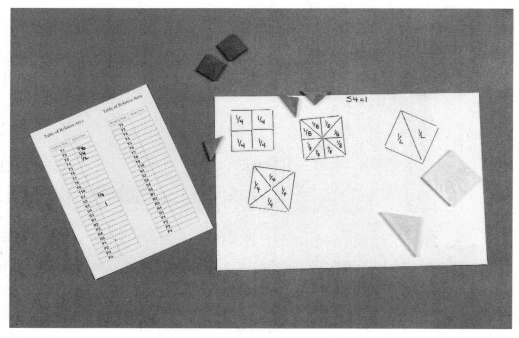

BUILDING FRACTIONAL AREAS

Materials: _____ Power Blocks
Unlined paper
Table of Relative Areas (blackline master)

Purpose: _____ To make shapes with fractional areas that have numerators larger than one

Activity: _____ Students complete a Table of Relative Areas for R5 equal to one square unit of area.

Teacher: Take out R5 and trace it on a piece of paper. Cover part of R5 with five R1s. What fraction of R5 is covered by R1s?
Student: Five-eighths.
Teacher: Right. Trace the R1s on top of your tracing of the R5 to show how they cover five-eighths of R5. Color the five-eighths part of your tracing. Take out three T3s, and put them on top of the R5. What fraction of R5 is covered by T3s?
Student: Three-fourths.

When students understand what is required, they cover part of R5 as many different way as they can with smaller identical blocks. They record their results.

Questions to explore with students:

- Can you generate fractions with numerators larger than one, if R3 = 1?
- Choose any block and make it equal to one square unit of area. Can you generate fractions with numerators larger than one?

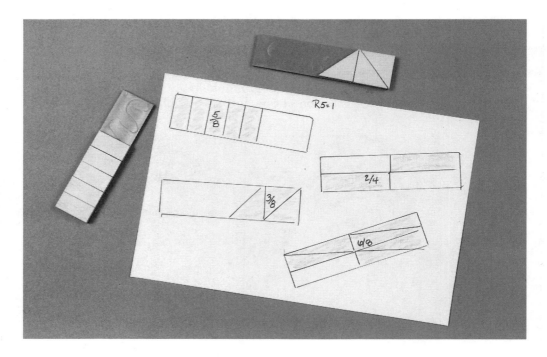

BUILDING SHAPES WITH AREAS THAT ARE MIXED NUMBERS

Materials: _____ Power Blocks
Unlined paper

Purpose: _____ To build shapes that have areas that are mixed numbers and to provide additional experience with the arbitrary nature of the definition of one whole unit

Activity: _____ **Teacher**: Today we are going to make shapes that have areas that are mixed numbers. A mixed number is a number that is a whole number, like two, combined with a fraction, like one-half. Define one square unit of area with any block you want except T1.
Student: Any block?
Teacher: Yes. Now make a shape that has an area of two and one-half. What blocks did you use?
Student: Two S4s and one T4.
Teacher: Did anyone make two and one-half a different way?
Student: Yes, I did it with two P2s and one P1.
Teacher: Make two and one-half as many different ways as you can? You may choose any block to be one square unit.

When students understand what is expected, they work independently building specific mixed numbers generated by the class (for example 1 3/4). They may change the definition of one square unit as they deem necessary. Students may make labels on slips of paper to identify the various groups of blocks, or they may make a record of their work by tracing and labeling the blocks in their drawings.

Questions to explore with students:

- Make a mixed number. Ask a neighbor to determine "one".
- If your neighbor tells you the mixed number, could you determine what "one" was? If so how?

EQUIVALENT FRACTIONS

Materials: _____ Power Blocks
Graph Paper (blackline master)
Table of Relative Areas (blackline master)

Purpose: _____ To create a list of equivalent fractions

Activity: _____ Students complete a Table of Relative Areas for S5 equal to one square unit of area.

Teacher: Take out P3. What is the area of P3? Use your Table of Relative Areas to get the answer.
Student: One-fourth.
Teacher: Is it possible to cover P3 with two triangles?
Student: Yes. Two T3s.
Teacher: What is the area of T3? Use your table to get the answer.
Student: One-eighth.
Teacher: Right. How many eighths did it take to cover P3?
Student: Two.
Teacher: I want you to record your results like this on the graph paper:

$$P3 = 1/4 = 2/8$$

How many T2s does it take to cover P3?
Student: Four.
Teacher: What is the area of T2?
Student: One-sixteenth.
Teacher: Record your results like this:

$$P3 = 1/4 = 2/8 = 4/16$$

Teacher: Are there any other ways to cover P3 with triangles?

Students choose another block and explore it in the same way. This exploration continues for each block in the set. Students are always to look for the number of smaller blocks that make larger blocks. The teacher saves the results of student explorations and consolidates them into a table. When students understand what is required, they collect the data and create their own tables for any definition of one square unit of area.

Questions to explore with students:

- Look at the table I have made from data you have given me. Do you see a pattern?
- If you knew the area of a block, could you predict the equivalent fractions that could be made with other blocks?
- Do you see a pattern that would enable you to make a list of equivalent fractions for any fraction?

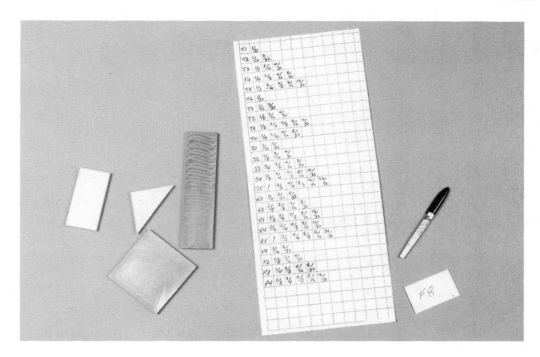

EQUIVALENT FRACTIONS - TRADING DOWN

Materials: _____ Power Blocks
Table of Relative Areas (blackline master)
Unlined paper

Purpose: _____ To identify specific equivalent fractions by trading larger blocks for smaller blocks

Activity: _____ Students complete a Table of Relative Areas for S5 equal to one square unit of area.

Teacher: Make a shape that has an area of 3/4 of a square unit. How did you do it?
Student: I used three R2s.
Teacher: Did anyone do it a different way?
Student: I use three P3s.
Teacher: Are there any other ways to make 3/4?
Student: I did it with three T3s and three T10s.
Teacher: Can you trade the blocks in your 3/4 for smaller blocks with the same shape and still have the same total area?
Student: I can trade my three R2s for six R1s.
Teacher: How much is one R1?
Student: One-eighth.
Teacher: How many eighths did it take to make 3/4?
Student: Six.
Teacher: Did anyone do it a different way?
Student: I traded three T3s for six T2s.
Teacher: Record it by tracing what you have done and writing the results like this:

$$3\ T3s = 3/4 = 6/8 =$$
$$or$$
$$3\ P3s = 3/4 = 6/8 =$$
$$or$$
$$3\ R3s = 3/4 = 6/8 =$$

Are there other identical smaller blocks that are equivalent to 6/8?

When students understand the process of trading down to smaller blocks that have the same total area as the starting area, the teacher and the class generate a series of fractions for the class to explore (for example: 3/8, 5/8, 3/16, 5/16, 7/16).

Questions to explore with students:

– Do you see a pattern that would enable you to make a list of equivalent fractions for any starting fraction?

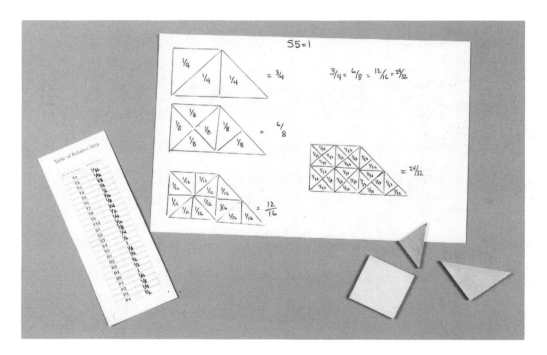

EQUIVALENT FRACTIONS - TRADING UP

Materials: _____ Power Blocks
Lined paper
Table of Relative Areas

Purpose: _____ To trade groups of identical smaller blocks for larger blocks

Activity: _____ Students complete a Table of Relative Area for S5 equal to one square unit of area.

Teacher: You need seven T2s. How many T2s does it take to make a T3?
Student: Two.
Teacher: Trade as many of your seven T2s for as many T3s as you can? How many T3s did you get?
Student: Three.
Teacher: Did you have any blocks left over?
Student: Yes. One T2.
Teacher: Look at your Table of Relative Areas, what is the area of T2?
Student: One-sixteenth.
Teacher: How many sixteenths did we start with?
Student: Seven.
Teacher: What is the area of T3?
Student: One-eighth.
Teacher: How many eighths did you have when you finished trading?
Student: Three.
Teacher: How many sixteenths did you have when you finished trading?
Student: One.
Teacher: Here is how to make a record of what you have done:

$$7 \ T2s = 7/16 = 3/8 + 1/16$$

When students understand the process of trading smaller blocks up for larger blocks, they create there own problems by taking arbitrary amounts of identical smaller blocks and trading until they can trade no more. For example if they started with nine T1s, they would go through the following series of trades:

$$9 \ T1s = 9/32 = 4/16 + 1/32$$

$$9 \ T1s = 9/32 = 2/8 + 1/32$$

$$9 \ T1s = 9/32 = 1/4 + 1/32$$

Questions to explore with students:

- If R4 = 1, can you create addition problems in the same way you did for the previous problems?
- Were there any situations in which you could not trade up?
- If you knew the fractions on the right side of the equations, could you use the blocks to determine what the starting fraction may have been?

EQUIVALENT FRACTIONS - TRADING UP (SIMPLIFYING)

Materials: _____ Power Blocks
Unlined paper
Table of Relative Areas (blackline master)

Purpose: _____ To identify equivalent fractions by trading smaller blocks for larger blocks (simplifying)

Activity: _____ Students complete a Table of Relative Area for S5 equal to one square unit of area.

Teacher: Yesterday when we were trading up, you could trade some of your blocks or all of your blocks. Today, we can only make trades if we can trade all of our blocks. This is called simplifying. Take out four R1s. What is the combined area of four R1s?
Student: Four-sixteenths.
Teacher: Can you trade the 4/16s for identical larger blocks?
Student: Yes. I can trade two R1s for an R2.
Teacher: How many R2s did you use to make trades?
Student: Two.
Teacher: How would you write two R2s as a fraction?
Student: Two-eighths.
Teacher: Can you trade the R2s for larger blocks.
Student: Yes, one R4.
Teacher: Did anyone do it a different way?
Student: Yes, I did it with one R3.
Teacher: What are the areas of R3 and R4?
Student: They are both 1/4.
Teacher: Record by tracing what you have done and writing the results like this:

$$4 \ R1s = 4/16 = 2/8 = 1/4$$

When students understand the process of trading all their smaller blocks up to larger blocks that have the same total area as the area of the blocks they started with, the teacher and class generate a list of fractions to explore (for example: 2/16, 6/16, 8/16, 12/16, 2/8, 4/8, 6/8, 2/4).

Questions to explore with students:

– If R4 = 1, create fractions of your choice. Which of your fractions can be simplified? Which ones cannot be simplified?

– Do you see a pattern that would enable you to predict fractions that can be simplified and those that cannot be simplified?

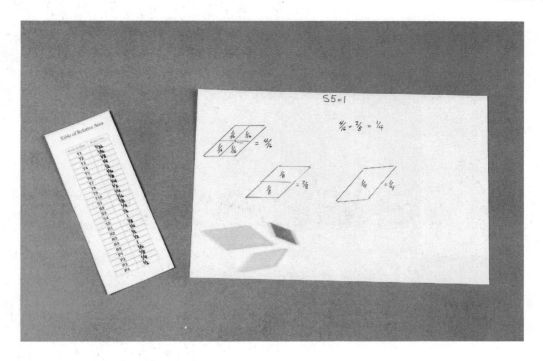

ADDITION - SAME DENOMINATORS

Materials: _____ Power Blocks
Table of Relative Areas (blackline master)
Unlined paper

Purpose: _____ To add the areas of congruent blocks

Activity: _____ Students complete a Table of Relative Area for S5 equal to one square unit of area.

Teacher: Take out two T4s. What is the area of one T4?
Student: One-fourth.
Teacher: What is the area of the two T4s if we combine them into one shape?
Student: Two-fourths.
Teacher: Can you simplify your answer by trading the two T4s for another block?
Student: Yes, I traded it for one T5.

When students understand what is required, they generate their own addition problems by combining congruent blocks into a single shape. The teacher can control the difficulty of the problems by limiting the number of blocks students can use in a given problem. They may record their work by tracing the blocks and writing equations. They may simplify their solutions by trading up if they wish.

Questions to explore with students:

– If you changed the definition of one square unit of area, could you generate different problems?
– Do you see a pattern that would enable you to predict the solution to addition problems in which the denominators are the same?

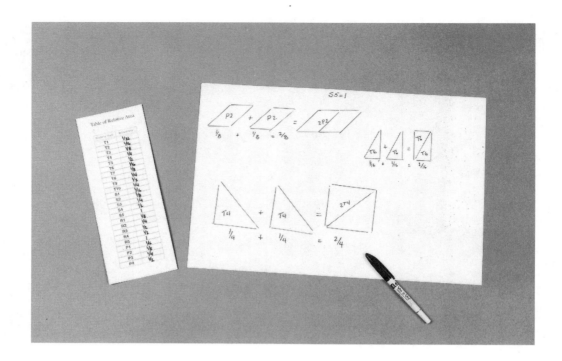

SUBTRACTION - SAME DENOMINATORS

Materials: _____ Power Blocks
Table of Relative Areas
Unlined paper

Purpose: _____ To create and subtract shapes using congruent blocks

Activity: _____ Students complete a Table of Relative Area for S5 equal to one square unit of area.

Teacher: Make a shape using four P2s, and record what you have done by tracing it.
Student: Do we just trace the outline, or do we show each little shape that makes the big shape?
Teacher: Show the little shapes. What is the area of the shape you have made?
Student: Four-eighths.
Teacher: Now take away one of the P2s. What is the area of the shape that remains?
Student: Three-eighths.
Teacher: Record what you have done by shading the blocks that you took away. Then write the equation like this:

$$4/8 - 1/8 = 3/8$$

When students understand what is expected, they independently create their own shapes and subtract congruent blocks of their choice from the larger shape.

Questions to explore with students:

– If you changed the definition of one square unit of area, could you generate different problems?

– Do you see a pattern that would enable you to predict the solution to subtraction problems in which the denominators are the same?

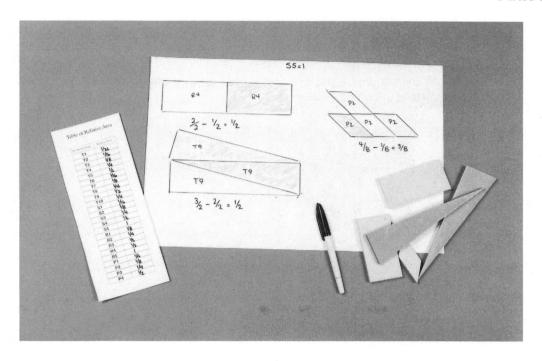

ADDITION - DIFFERENT DENOMINATORS

Materials: _____ Power Blocks
Unlined paper
Table of Relative Areas (blackline master)

Purpose: _____ To have students generate addition problems using blocks

Activity: _____ Students complete a Table of Relative Area for S5 equal to one square unit of area.

Teacher: Take out T5 and T4. Make a shape using the two blocks. What is the area of T5?
Student: One-half.
Teacher: What is the area of T4?
Student: One-fourth.
Teacher: Trace T5 on your piece of paper. Put a plus sign after it. Trace T4 next to the plus sign. Put an equals sign after the T4. Then trace the combined shape after the equals sign. Write the shapes' areas beneath each tracing. The two fractions have different denominators. What could you do to get the denominators the same?
Student: Trade T5 down for two T4s.
Teacher: If we do that, what is the area of the shape we combined from T5 and T4?
Student: Three-fourths.
Teacher: Record your work as an equation.

When students understand what is expected they independently create their own addition problems by taking blocks at random and combining them to make a single shape. They record their work by tracing what they have done, and writing an equation. The difficulty of the shapes students choose to build may be controlled by limiting the number of blocks they may use.

Questions to explore with students:

- If you changed the definition of one square unit of area, could you generate different problems?
- Do you see a pattern that would enable you to predict the common denominator for any problem you create?

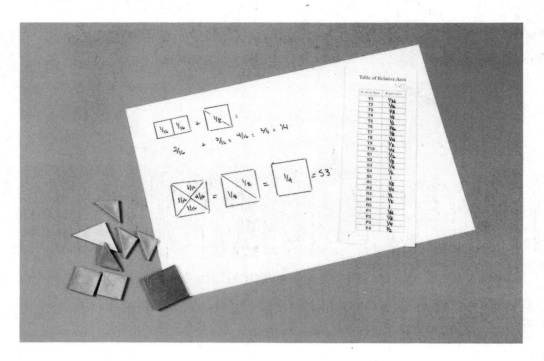

SUBTRACTION - DIFFERENT DENOMINATORS

Materials: _____ Power Blocks
Unlined paper
Table of Relative Areas (blackline master)

Purpose: _____ To have students generate their own subtraction problems.

Activity: _____ Students complete a Table of Relative Area for S5 equal to one square unit of area.

Teacher: Take out P4. Trace it. What is the area of P4?
Student: One-half.
Teacher: Take out T4. What is the area of T4?
Student: One-fourth.
Teacher: Cover part of P4 with T4. Trace what you have done. Shade the part of the drawing that is covered by T4. This is the way I want you to show the part of P4 we are subtracting. How could we show what we have done with numbers?
Student: Write: one-half minus one-fourth.
Teacher: Suppose we wanted both fractions to have the same denominators. What could we do?
Student: Trade P4 for two T4s. Then all the blocks would have the same denominators.

Teacher: How could we write that?
Student: Two-fourths minus one-fourth.
Teacher: What is left after we subtract the one-fourth?
Student: One-fourth.

When the students understand the process, they generate their own subtraction problems. They select a block and place a smaller block on top of it. They record their work with drawings and equations.

Questions to explore with students:

– If you changed the definition of one square unit of area, could you generate different problems?
– Do you see a pattern that would enable you to predict the common denominator for any problem you create?

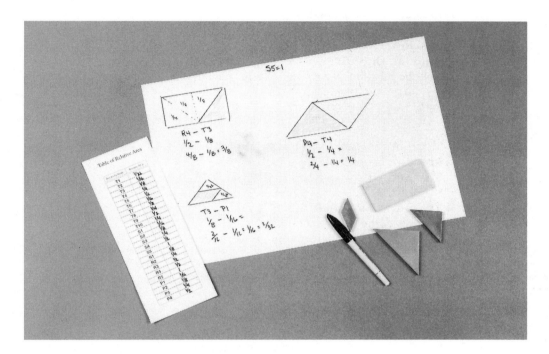

MULTIPLICATION OF FRACTIONS

Materials:_____ Power Blocks
Lined paper
Table of Relative Areas

Purpose: _____ To have students find the answers to problems like, "What is 1/2 of 1/4?"

Activity: _____ Students complete a Table of Relative Area for S5 equal to one square unit of area.

Teacher: Take out S5. What is the area of S5?
Student: One.
Teacher: What is one-half of S5?
Student: T5.
Teacher: What is the area of T5?
Student: One-half.
Teacher: I want you to record your results like this:

1/2 of 1 = 1/2

Take out P1. What is the area of P1?
Student: One-sixteenth.
Teacher: What is one-half of P1?
Student: T1.
Teacher: What is the area of T1?
Student: One-thirty-second.
Teacher: Add this information to your table.

1/2 of 1 = 1/2
1/2 of 1/16 = 1/32

When the class understands the process, they are asked to find 1/2 of the area for as many blocks as they can. When they have done this, they are asked to find 1/4 of the area for as many blocks in the set as they can. They do the same thing for 1/8s and 1/16s. The data is added to their list.

The teacher carefully selects other problems for the class to explore because not all problems can be done with the blocks. Examples of other problems to explore are: What is 3/8 of R4, 3/4 of P4, 5/8 of T4?

Questions to explore with students:

– Do you see a pattern that you could use to predict the answer to questions like, "What is three-eighths of one-fourth"?

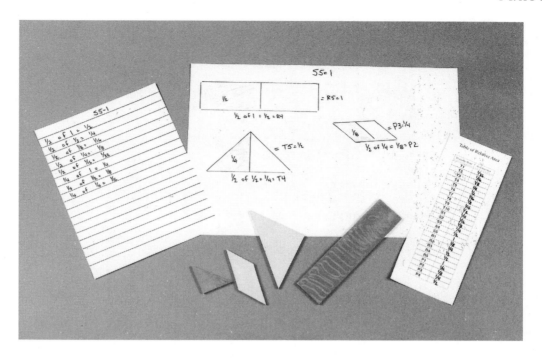

DIVISION OF FRACTIONS

Materials: _____ Power Blocks
Lined paper
Table of Relative Areas (blackline master)

Purpose: _____ To have students determine how many blocks of a specified area are in another block

Activity: _____ Students complete a Table of Relative Area for S5 equal to one square unit of area.

Teacher: Here is how I want you to record what we are about to do. Make three columns on your paper. Write your headings like this:

Large piece   Small piece   Number

Take out S5. What is the area of S5?
Student: One.
Teacher: Record it like this:

Large piece   Small piece   Number
1

Take out T5. What is the area of T5?

Student: One-half.
Teacher: Record it like this:

Large piece   Small piece   Number
1   1/2

How many T5s are in the S5?
Student: Two.
Teacher: Record it like this:

Large piece	Small piece	Number
1	1/2	2

Take out T4. What is the area of T4?
Student: One-fourth.
Teacher: How many T4s are in S5?
Student: Four.
Teacher: Record it like this:

Large piece	Small piece	Number
1	1/2	2
1	1/4	4

When the class understands the process, they are asked to create problems in which they find the number of smaller blocks in a larger block. They add the information to their table.

Questions to explore with students:

– Do you see a pattern that will enable you to predict the number of times a block will go into another block?

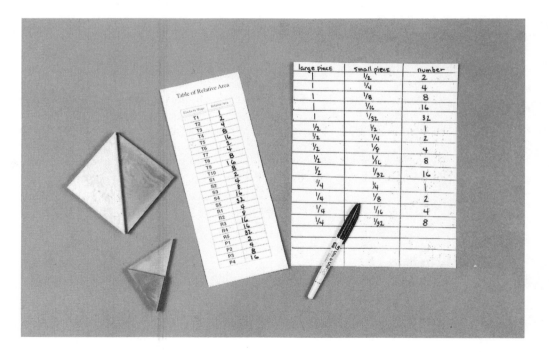

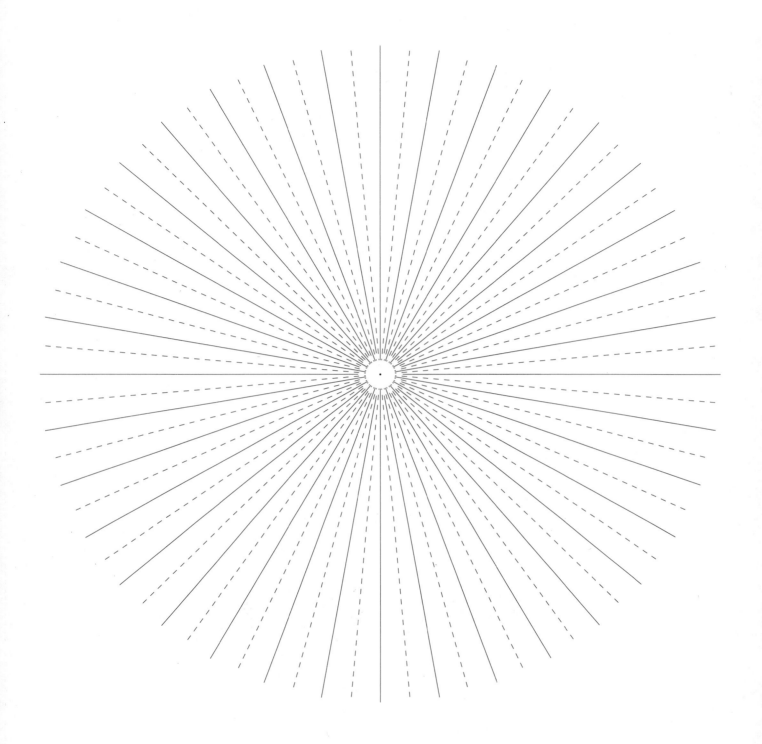

Protractor Blackline

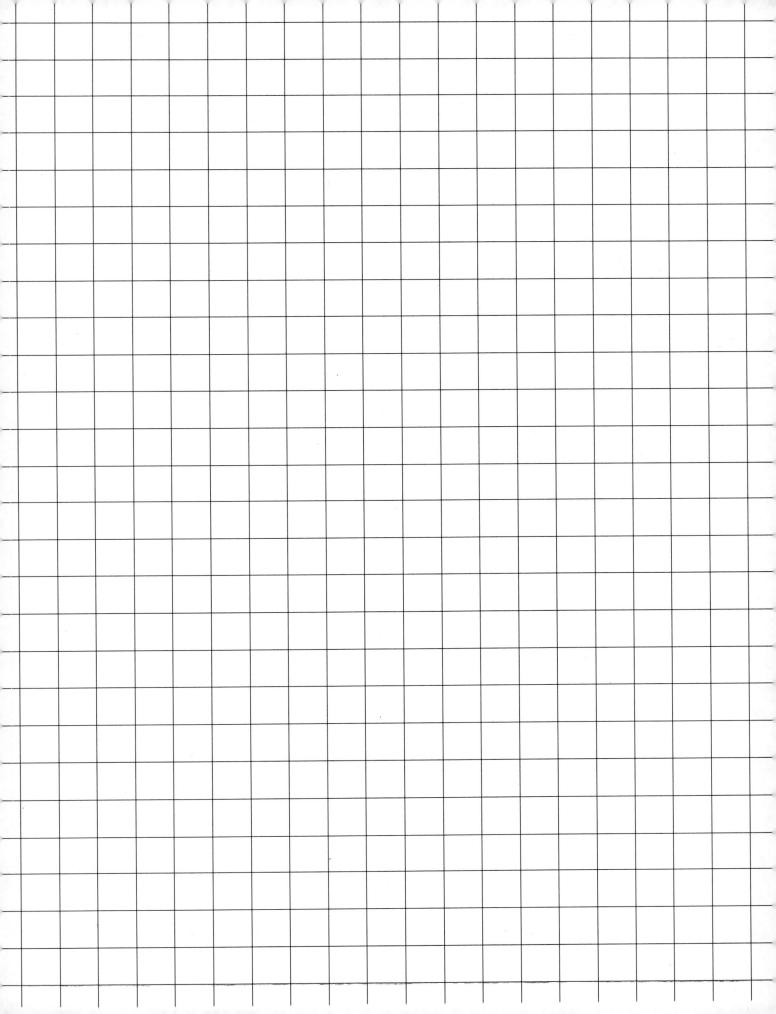

Power Block Triangle Blackline

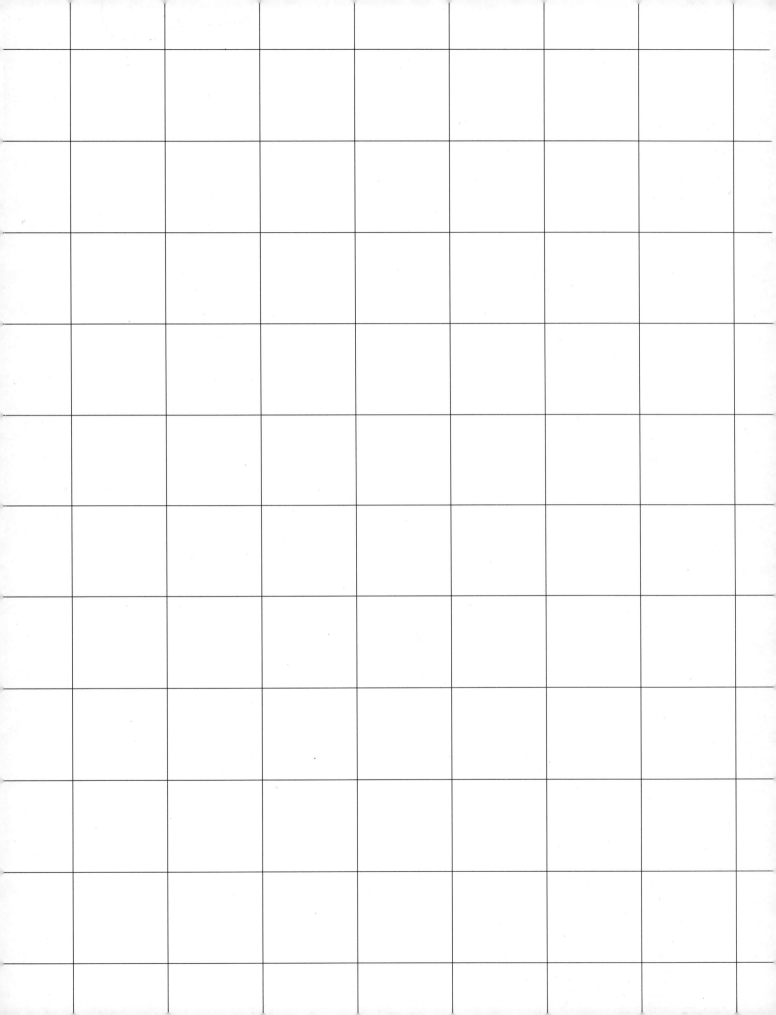

Powerblock Blackline

Table of Relative Areas

Blocks by Size	Relative Area
T1	
T2	
T6	
S1	
P1	
T3	
T7	
S2	
R1	
P2	
T4	
T8	
T10	
S3	
R2	
P3	
T5	
T9	
S4	
R3	
R4	
P4	
S5	
R5	

Table of Relative Areas

Blocks by Size	Relative Area
T1	
T2	
T6	
S1	
P1	
T3	
T7	
S2	
R1	
P2	
T4	
T8	
T10	
S3	
R2	
P3	
T5	
T9	
S4	
R3	
R4	
P4	
S5	
R5	

Table of Relative Areas

Blocks by Shape	Relative Area
T1	
T2	
T3	
T4	
T5	
T6	
T7	
T8	
T9	
T10	
S1	
S2	
S3	
S4	
S5	
R1	
R2	
R3	
R4	
R5	
P1	
P2	
P3	
P4	

Table of Relative Areas

Blocks by Shape	Relative Area
T1	
T2	
T3	
T4	
T5	
T6	
T7	
T8	
T9	
T10	
S1	
S2	
S3	
S4	
S5	
R1	
R2	
R3	
R4	
R5	
P1	
P2	
P3	
P4	

Metric Tangram Blackline

Powerblock Blackline